West Virginia
State Facts

Nickname:	The Mountain State
Date Entered Union:	June 20, 1863 (the 35th state)
Motto:	*Montani semper liberi* (Mountaineers are always free)
West Virginia Men:	George Brett, *baseball player* Thomas "Stonewall" Jackson, *Confederate general* Don Knotts, *actor* Peter Marshall, *TV host* Chuck Yeager, *air force general*
Bird:	Cardinal
Flower:	Rhododendron
Fun Facts:	Mother's Day was first proclaimed in West Virginia in 1908.
	When Laurie Paige's friend Judy invited her to her daughter's wedding, Laurie discovered the difference between a "crik" and a river and a "hollow" and a valley in order to reach The Farm.

The Forbidden Fruit

So how come apples got the blame for the fall of mankind?

Probably because they've been around since time began.

The charred remains of apples were found in prehistoric lake dwellings in Europe. The first still-life paintings were of apples, carved on cave walls thousands of years ago. On tablets drawn up in China, Babylon and Egypt, apples were depicted as an important harvest, used as gifts and banquet food.

The apple appears in the mythology, history and traditions of nearly every ancient nation. It's written about in the Bible, the Hindu *Code of Manu* and the Egyptian *Book of the Dead*.

We eat apples raw, baked, fried and pureed into sauce. We cook them in fritters, dumplings and pies. We grow them in several hundred, perhaps a thousand, varieties in nearly every country on earth.

Maybe we're still trying to become wise!

American

HEROES

AGAINST ALL ODDS

Laurie
PAIGE

Cara's Beloved

Silhouette Books

Published by Silhouette Books
America's Publisher of Contemporary Romance

To my friend Judy,
with thanks for the tales of West Virginia.

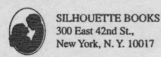 SILHOUETTE BOOKS
300 East 42nd St.,
New York, N. Y. 10017

ISBN 0-373-82246-4

CARA'S BELOVED

Copyright © 1993 by Olivia M. Hall

This edition published by arrangement with Harlequin Books S.A.

® and TM are trademarks of Harlequin Books S.A., used under license. Trademarks indicated with ® are registered in the United States Patent and Trademark Office, the Canadian Trade Marks Office and in other countries.

Visit Silhouette at www.eHarlequin.com

Printed in U.S.A.

About the Author

Laurie Paige says, "One of the nicest things about writing romances is researching locales, careers and ideas. In the interest of authenticity, most writers will try anything...once." Along with her writing adventures, Laurie has been a NASA engineer, a past president of the Romance Writers of America (twice!), a mother and a grandmother (twice, also!). She was twice a Romance Writers of American RITA Award finalist for Best Traditional Romance and has won awards from *Romantic Times Magazine* for Best Silhouette Special Edition and Best Silhouette. She has also been presented with *Affaire de Coeur's* Readers Choice Silver Pen Award for Favorite Contemporary Author. Recently resettled in Northern California, Laurie is looking to whatever experiences her next novel will send her on.

Dear Reader,

For me, every new story begins with a "what if" situation, then I sit back and watch the possibilities unfold. For instance, what if there's this guy named Adam who lives in Paradise—Paradise Falls, West Virginia, to be exact. He surely has to expect problems. After all, every Eden has a troublemaker.

But trouble is pretty hard to identify when it comes in the guise of your first love.

When Cara Gardner agrees to evaluate the antiques at his family mansion and at the old clothing mill his family started generations ago, Adam expects their relationship to proceed on a professional basis. That's all. (Men can be so dense!)

However, he takes one look and is consumed with a desire to sample this delectable forbidden fruit that was denied him years ago....

Sit back, take a big bite of a deliciously crisp apple from Paradise and enjoy!

Laurie Paige

Please address questions and book requests to:
Silhouette Reader Service
U.S.: 3010 Walden Ave., P.O. Box 1325, Buffalo, NY 14269
Canadian: P.O. Box 609, Fort Erie, Ont. L2A 5X3

Chapter One

Cara Gardner stopped the van on the high bluff of Vista Point and gazed at the town lying in the protective cradle of three mountain peaks. Paradise Falls, West Virginia.

She tried to view the small community from an equally high and remote emotional distance. It was impossible. She'd been born in Paradise Falls. She'd grown to adolescence there. She'd fallen in love there.

Youthful dreams—wildly romantic and blindly confident of the future—flooded her memory. All those impossible schemes had been shattered at the arrest of her father for embezzling funds from the Clairmont textile mill. Although he'd been released due to lack of evidence, their lives had irrevocably changed from that day forward. Respect, friendship, their home, all were gone.

Cara's trust in life, in the *fairness* of things, had also been shattered. She'd recovered, but not without realizing she'd lost more than dreams and a comfortable way of life. Perhaps some things, she mused, were never meant to be.

The sudden sting of tears in her eyes surprised her. She drew four deep breaths—the way the high school English teacher had taught them to do before a speech—and tried to relax. Memories weren't the only reason for the taut state of her nerves.

She had a personal reason for returning to the scene of her family's humiliation. She wanted, if at all possible, to find the person who had taken that money and darkened her father's name.

"Stephen Gardner was the most honest man who ever lived," her mother had declared in angry despair after his death five years ago. "I hope the person who took that money never has a moment's joy from using it. If only we knew who did it," she'd cried.

Comforting her mother in their mutual grief, Cara had vowed she would someday return to Paradise Falls and totally exonerate her father by ferreting out the truth. At last she had her chance.

For the hundredth time, she pondered the letter she'd received from Adam Clairmont asking for an evaluation of the antiques at his home. Adam was the son of the previous owner of the mill. His father was dead now, too, and Adam headed up the company that turned out fine woven cotton that was used mostly for men's shirts.

A chill of foreboding rushed over her as she contemplated the possible reasons he'd written to *her*. Maybe, like Scrooge, people were never prepared to face the ghosts of their pasts, she brooded. She certainly felt she wasn't.

Well, misgivings aside, she had a job to do for the Townsend Antique Appraisal and Auction Company.

That task she would perform. Her personal goal might or might not be accomplished.

Blinking away the tears and the memories, she backed her vehicle from the bluff and headed down the ridge into the rocky valley below.

Cara found Paradise Falls just as she remembered. It had some new store fronts, but nothing was drastically different from eight years ago, when she and her family had moved away. She'd been eighteen at the time. And had lived a lifetime since.

She drove past the elementary school where she'd had a crush on the new science teacher for the whole of sixth grade. Her vision blurred as tears formed again. She frowned, disconcerted by the emotion that churned inside her. She needed to be in control.

Turning onto Main Street, she observed the changes with an outsider's critical eye. The movie house had closed. It had been turned into an arcade of small craft and gift shops which should appeal to the tourist trade, assuming there was one.

The Asher mansion was now an inn. The ancient New River Hotel, which had been closed when she was a child, was remodeled into stores and offices. A sign in a window advertised mule trips into the mountains for the adventure seeker.

Her heart lurched as she turned into Mill Street. The imposing red brick front of Clairmont Textiles beamed down on her like a benign tyrant. It was the town's reason for being, the economic mainstay of the community, and had been for generations.

She drove slowly up the broad street and pulled into a parking space marked Visitors. The wind jerked at her wool skirt and swirled away her body heat when she stepped onto the pavement.

After debating whether she should throw her heavy coat over her shoulders, she decided not to bother and walked swiftly toward the ornately carved wooden door with the three glass panes running down the middle. She could remember dashing from the car when she was little and peering in the lowest one to see if her father was coming down the hall.

The beveled edges of the glass caught the weak April sun and scattered the light into rainbows. For a moment she stared through the clear panes of the door as if she were a child again. Her heart beat furiously against her ribs. She fought an impulsive desire to run....

Adam dropped the pen on the desk pad and rose to his feet when the van stopped and Clara climbed out. He'd wondered how he would react upon seeing her again. Now he knew. At the first sight of her, desire had hit him like a blow to the midsection...well, maybe a little lower. He smiled wryly, with little humor.

Still watching her, he drew four slow breaths. Then coolly, analytically—the manner in which he'd learned to view life and its idiosyncrasies the past few years—he compared her with the person he'd once known.

All the feminine promise of her adolescence had matured into a graceful woman of average height. Her figure was good...more than good—perfect. She wore a blue sweater and a plaid skirt with a matching scarf tied around her shoulders. Her hair swirled in the wind, its auburn highlights turning to flame in the sun.

When she wrapped her arms across her chest against the cold, his cool appraisal was sidetracked. For a moment he remembered precisely how she'd felt in his arms—her response eager and loving—and that he'd wanted her with a passion so intense it had burned clear to his soul.

He smiled again. He'd gotten over his poetic inclinations years ago. Life had stripped those early expectations from him inch by searing inch. Cara had helped. He would never again wear his heart on his sleeve for any woman.

The cold wind seemed to penetrate the glass pane as he watched her hurry across the parking lot toward the building. Once more he questioned his sanity in writing her that letter. His reasons were sound enough, he assured himself. Had there been another motive in the back of his mind? Hardly.

This was business. He had need of her services as an appraiser, nothing more. The problems at the mill were the most pressing concern in his life at the present. He had no time for the past. He went to the door to welcome her.

Cara stifled the desire to flee when the massive door opened and a never-forgotten male voice remarked in tones as chilling as the wind that blew down her neck, "So, you're here."

She stared at the man before her. Adam.

For a second she saw him as he had once been—Adam Clairmont, star running back of the Paradise Falls Falcons, brilliant student at Harvard Law School, sole heir to Clairmont Textiles, Inc. He was also Adam Clairmont, son of the man who had questioned her father's innocence and broken his heart.

He'd been twenty-one the last time they'd met, on the steps of the courthouse right after the investigation, and he was looking at her in much the same way he had then—his eyes cold, their depths darkened by emotions she couldn't read. Cara had turned from him then. She almost did now.

"Hello, Adam," she said.

She noticed that neither of them smiled. A shiver rushed over her. She drew a deep breath and hugged her arms across her again, aware of the cold and the penetrating quality of his gaze.

Fear tingled along her scalp and down her spine. She felt he could see all the way inside her and knew her real reason for accepting this job.

He stepped back to let her in, then closed the door behind them, shutting out the wind. "I wasn't sure you'd show."

He smiled then, and she was struck by the cynical nature of it. This was an Adam she didn't know, she realized, a man hardened by events she hadn't shared. Again she drew in a deep breath, seeking calm. She saw his chest move as if he did the same. Was he a little nervous about seeing her again?

And what, she wondered, were his memories of them? Were they as tender and poignant and painful as hers? His cool once-over cured her of that notion. This man was light-years from the boy she'd known. He was hard, skeptical and self-contained.

"Oh?" she questioned, managing just the right amount of polite curiosity in her tone, she thought.

His grin widened. "If I remember correctly, at our last meeting you said you never wanted to see me again."

So he did remember...and found it amusing. Her

composure wavered a bit. "That was a long time ago."

"A long time," he echoed.

"And this is business." People always accepted that excuse.

Adam studied her another moment. "So it is." He gestured toward an open doorway a few feet down the hall. "I have fresh coffee in my office. It'll take the chill out."

She looked at his hands. They were broad across the palm, and his fingers were lean and supple. Hands told a lot about the character of a person, her mother believed. Adam's were strong. They looked capable of inflicting pain. Cara knew they could also be gentle, even as passion consumed him.

The tears pressed close to the surface. She glanced away, an instinctive sense of sorrow echoing hollowly through her. This was much harder than she'd imagined it would be.

She glanced at her watch. "It's almost four. I think I'd prefer to get settled in, if you'll tell me where I'm registered. Your secretary said she would handle it."

He ran a hand through his hair, which was already going silver in the usual Clairmont manner, and pushed it off his forehead. A frown tweaked a line between his brows. "I thought you would stay at the house. I mean, I thought it would be easier for you to be on the premises. For your work."

Cara looked away from his keen gaze. The vivid contrast of his gray eyes with their dark perimeter and the black hair threaded with silver was alluring. The way his hair insisted on feathering over his forehead induced a woman to push it back just to watch it shift forward again, she admitted, but the years had added a hardness to his features that dared a woman to take that intimacy.

She glanced at his mouth. It was beautifully molded. His lips could be gentle, passionate, or both. She caught back the thought. Adam as a lover wasn't part of her plans.

She was overreacting to his nearness, to the handsome leanness of his build, the intelligence in his glance, the strength that made her want to seek his embrace.

Being here, in the town of her family's disgrace, made her much too vulnerable, she realized. Forcing a smile, she said, "That's kind of you, but I wouldn't want to impose on you and Mrs. Clairmont."

"My mother lives in Florida now."

"I meant your wife," she said stiffly.

He shook his head, his hair settling further across his brow. "I don't have one, but there's a housekeeper, Mrs. Groves, who stays at the house now that she's a widow. You may remember her."

Cara remembered. Mrs. Groves had fed her cookies and milk on more than one visit to the Clairmont mansion. "Yes, I remember her well," she said. She followed him into the office.

He poured two cups of coffee and indicated the sugar packets in a bowl. "Help yourself. I think there's milk." He opened the door to a small refrigerator and peered inside.

She decided to drink it plain. Her hands weren't too steady, and she'd probably spill sugar all over his old-fashioned oak desk. She picked up the cup with both hands. "This is fine."

Adam indicated a comfortable chair in front of his desk, waited until she sat down, then settled into his executive chair. Silence arced between them. "I appreciate your agreeing to work within my time frame," he said rather formally.

"It was no problem." Her schedule had been completely revised to meet his request. "I was surprised when I got your letter."

"More than surprised, I'd be willing to bet." Again his smile was cynical.

He would never know exactly how disturbed she'd been. She wasn't calm yet. "How did you know... that is, how did you hear of the company and my working there?"

The wind rattled the windows and hissed mournfully past the building. She glanced out and saw clouds gathering, playing hide-and-seek with the sun. Like the wind, she felt restless.

"I saw Miss Josie at the Historical Society meeting," he explained. "She said you'd done some excellent work for her sister in Beckley last year. I asked her to get the address for me."

"I see."

"I understand your stepfather owns the company?"

Cara nodded. "Yes. I became an appraiser for him after I got my fine arts degree. He taught me the business."

"You went to work for him after your mother's marriage?" Adam inquired. His eyes skimmed over her, then lingered on her sweater. Her skin burned under the blue acrylic knit.

His gaze shifted and rested on her lips. She thought of kisses raining over her face, teasing her, of how hungry her mouth had once been for his.

"No, I knew him first. Actually I've been working for him since the first year we moved to Roanoke. He

met my mother after I started working full-time. After
my father's heart attack.''

"I'm sorry about your father," Adam said.

She nodded, not sure how he meant it. "I heard
that your father had died, too. Mother subscribes to
the local paper and told me about it." Her tone con-
veyed her sympathy.

An awkward silence followed.

"Do you like your job?" he asked.

"Yes, it's fun. I'm very good at it," she added, on
the defensive in case he thought her frivolous.

"I don't doubt it."

She felt foolish at his amused tone. He was just
making conversation, but she felt dangerously on
edge. Perhaps her coming here wasn't such a good
idea. Perhaps she should have turned down Adam's
request.

When her mother, who ran the office and opened
all the mail, had gotten the letter, she'd taken it to
Cara immediately. They'd both realized the possibilities.

"Cara, do you think— Oh, if…if you could find
just one tiny clue…" Ann Gardner Townsend had
stumbled over her words in excitement.

In spite of her own misgivings, Cara hadn't been
able to disappoint the rekindled hope in her mother's
eyes by refusing the job.

A need to be alone, to sort her feelings and regain
control assailed her. She checked the time again and
found Adam's eyes on her when she looked up.

"We'd better see about a place for you," he said.
"If you'd really rather not stay at the house, the Asher
Inn might have a room, although I doubt it. Some
nature group arrived yesterday, a busload of them.

Personally I think they're crazy, wanting to go tromping through the woods in this weather.''

"They're probably going to count the hawks that are returning to nest, or something like that," she said.

Her father had taught her to look for them. Each spring they'd climbed the highest peak with a picnic lunch and watched for hours, eyes glued to the sky as the hawks came home to raise their young. As if she peered at the world from the hawk's lofty view, Cara saw herself returning to Paradise Falls, stopping at the lookout and gazing at the town of her birth.

She looked out the window, then back at Adam. Hawks mate for life, her father had told her.

"Maybe," Adam agreed, giving her a probing glance. "Look, I'll call the inn and a couple of bed and breakfast places—"

"No, don't," she requested, making a decision. Being at the house was perfect for the job and for her plans. She tried for an amused tone to match the one he'd used concerning the nature group. "The big house will be much more practical."

She realized she had slipped easily into the local manner of referring to the Clairmont house as the "big house."

Adam studied her for another few seconds, his clear gray gaze exploring her dark hair and smoky-blue eyes, then again settling on her lips, causing them to tingle. His expression seemed to harden, and he looked away. She detected anger in his manner.

"Good," he said. "Let me clear up some paperwork, and I'll see you home. I thought we would have dinner at the house and talk about the job. Unless you'd rather go out?"

"No, that's fine."

He picked up a sheaf of papers. The mill was so quiet she could have heard a pin drop. Although it was Saturday, she'd expected other people to be there. The cavernous building creaked and groaned in the wind like a haunted house.

Cara rubbed her neck. Sally Winetski, who'd been her best friend at Paradise Falls High all those years ago, would have said someone was tramping on her grave.

While Adam focused his attention on sorting and storing some reports in a file folder, Cara studied him. In a few months he would be thirty. She wondered about the women in his life—who they were, if he was serious about anyone, why he hadn't married one of the debs he'd met in college.

He glanced her way and caught her staring. Her smile was purposefully cool before she turned away to peruse his office and the simplicity of the decor.

"I thought you would have a big rolltop desk and glass-fronted bookcases," she blurted aloud, taking in his battered desk and plain oak cabinets.

"My father did. His office is upstairs. We don't use it anymore. I like to be closer to the door for a quick getaway when salesmen come around." Adam spoke in a light tone that didn't match his eyes. Again she had the sense she spoke to a stranger, not the man who'd once kissed her until neither of them could think....

"I see." She clenched her fingers together so he wouldn't notice the sudden tremor that attacked them. Slowly, carefully, she made herself relax. "Antique office furniture can be every bit as valuable as house furniture. Would you like me to check it over while I'm here?''

He locked his desk and pocketed the set of keys while staring at her thoughtfully. ''It might not hurt to know if it's worth anything. We have a warehouse full of junk. And a big attic at the house with stuff stored in it. I didn't think of that.''

''Perhaps I'll look here first, before I start at the house.'' Cara stood and moved toward the door when he did.

He nodded while putting his suit coat on, then indicated she was to precede him. He locked the massive door behind them when they stepped outside into the raw April wind.

She couldn't believe it was going to be this easy to get into the mill storerooms. She hugged her arms around her as ripples of apprehension danced over her. She felt so near the truth. Some clue awaited her in this town. She wanted desperately to find it.

''We might have snow tonight, if the temperature drops much lower. Or ice,'' he told her. ''I hope you brought a warm coat.''

''It's in the van,'' she replied and dashed toward the four-wheel-drive vehicle, a practical choice for her work since she often traveled mountain roads. She also bought antiques on the spot and needed transportation that could hold her purchases.

''Follow me to the house,'' he called after her.

Driving the steep, winding road to the Clairmont house a few minutes later, she sighed deeply, relieved at having that first face-to-face meeting with Adam behind her. It had bothered her more than she'd wanted to admit.

If she was to do her work *and* search for evidence,

she had to stay cool and keep her mind focused on her tasks. She couldn't let past emotions get in the way.

When they arrived at the massive brick mansion, Adam jumped out of the red Porsche, an old one his father used to drive, and came toward her. She wondered if he kept the flashy sports car for sentiment's sake. He and his father must have grown close during the two years they'd worked together at the mill.

Just as she and her father had been close, Cara reminded herself. She wouldn't feel pity for Adam and his loss. His griefs were no concern of hers. She climbed out of the van.

"Maybe you should look around before we take your luggage in," he suggested, giving her an odd look. Did her doubts and fears show on her face?

"No, I don't mind staying here. Really." Now that she had realized what an advantage it would be to have free rein in the house and at the mill, she tried not to seem too eager.

He shrugged and held out his hand for the key to open the back of the van. A minute later she followed him up the steps, carrying her cosmetic case in one hand and her briefcase in the other while he carried her one large piece of luggage.

Adam threw open the front door, a replica of the one at the mill, except it had a brass door knocker in the shape of some ancient god attached to it. She noted the door wasn't kept locked during the day.

"Good," he commented when he entered, "the heat's on." He held the door and waited for her to come in. "We've had some problems with the furnace. It's almost as ancient as the house."

She stepped into the hall, not sure what to expect,

but it was as she remembered. The Louis XV sideboard still stood next to the wall, the Fifth Dynasty vase still perched on a whatnot pedestal in the far corner, a marble stair curved gracefully into the upper regions of the house. It was like stepping back in time.

"Are you all right?" Adam asked. He had apparently decided candor was called for. "Does it bother you to come back here?"

All the spirits of the past seemed to be pressing against her chest. It was difficult to breathe. "No, of course not. It's just...everything is as lovely as I remembered." She made her smile casual. "Is my room upstairs?"

"First door to the right at the top of the steps. It has a view toward the front. You can see the whole town." He let the door swing closed silently behind him and went up the steps.

She followed, haunting visions of the past invading her mind. Each Christmas, she and her parents had been invited to this house when the Clairmonts gave a party for the managers at the company. A gift had always been waiting under the tree for her. Each spring there had been a gigantic Easter egg hunt, while in summer a picnic was held on the lawn. Her memories of this house were happy ones.

"Mrs. Groves is probably in the kitchen. She prepares breakfast and dinner. You're on your own for lunch and usually on the weekends." Adam explained the housekeeping arrangements as he entered the bedroom. "The flowers got here, I see. We thought the room might be...friendlier with some flowers."

Cara glanced at the pots of tulips and daffodils that lined the broad windowsill and adorned the brick hearth. She felt the tension increasing inside her. She needed to be alone. "That was thoughtful of you. Thank you very much," she said in dismissive tones.

"Is there anything else you'll need? Oh, the bathroom is through that door. And the intercom on the phone is connected to all the rooms, including my office at the mill. Dial nine to reach me here, ten to get me there. Dial one for the kitchen if you need Mrs. Groves. There's a list in the drawer."

"Yes, that's fine. Thank you." She put her cases down and laid her purse on a floral silk Queen Anne chair. Her fingers trembled, and she clenched them at her sides.

She was very sure her task was going to be much harder than she had expected. And she had expected it might be impossible.

"Here's a key to the front door. The house is rarely locked, so you probably won't need it too often." Adam held it out.

She took it, anxious for him to be gone.

"Well," he said, glancing around the room once more, "I'll see you at six for dinner."

"At six?"

"Is that too early for you?"

"Oh, no, that's all right." She realized her tone was too turbulent and moderated her voice. "I had an early lunch." A lie, she'd had no lunch at all. She hadn't been hungry. She still wasn't.

"I'll be in the library until then. Join me if you'd like. I'd be glad of the company." He looked out the window as if at a distant vision. "It's been a long spring."

The admission startled her. She stared at him while

he placed her pullman on a cedar chest under the sash, nodded briefly, then left.

Cara sat on a footstool that would probably date back to the seventeenth century at the very least and frowned as she considered the undercurrents that had run between her and Adam.

She would have to watch herself around him. It would be easy to forget his keen intellect and sharp perception, if she let herself be pulled back into old feelings for him.

Yet, in that instant when he'd looked out the window and remarked on the long spring, she couldn't shake the intuition that Adam was lonely.

Why should he be? her common sense demanded. He was the most eligible bachelor in town. There must be lots of women eager for his company. All the girls had sighed over him when she'd lived there, including her.

She reached deep inside for control as a tremor ran through her. She felt so open, so raw.

Naturally she was vulnerable here, she reminded herself. Adam and this house were tied to her family's hurt and disgrace. Now that she realized how affected she was at being back, she would be better able to handle the emotions thus generated.

A headache throbbed behind her eyes, and she pressed the heels of her hands against them. For a second the memories overpowered her attempt at control....

She'd just turned eighteen...Adam was twenty-one, almost twenty-two. It was June and school was out...he was home from college. Law school wasn't until the fall. A bunch of kids had gone to the river for swimming and an impromptu picnic...Adam had been there. She'd cut her foot on a broken bottle, and he'd volunteered to drive her to the clinic, then home....

Her head pounded, and she pressed harder against her eyes, not wanting to remember the glory and heartache of first love.

Adam looked at the big grandfather clock standing against one wall of the library. The minute hand had moved exactly one mark since the last time he'd checked. It was ten minutes before six.

He put aside the local newspaper. He shouldn't have sent that letter. It had been a damned fool thing to do—he castigated himself for his poor judgment. "Let sleeping dogs lie" was a wise old saying. He should have heeded it.

Seeing Cara stirred old memories...old passions. Damn! Eight years, and that hadn't changed. He still wanted her.

That long-ago summer, he hadn't let himself take advantage of her inexperience, her tender offering of herself to the wild, nearly uncontrollable feelings between them. He'd nobly reminded himself that he had three years of law school ahead of him before they could possibly marry.

The irony of his former idealism didn't escape him. In those days he'd thought there was time for them, all the time in the world, with paradise yet to come. He'd had a lot to learn.

Her reluctance to stay at the house gnawed at him. Did she still hate him because of what had happened to her father?

Well, it was all water under the bridge.

He mocked the thought. He was full of wisdom

today, it seemed. Where had it been when he was writing that damned letter?

For a moment his thoughts veered into the dangerous territory of the past. He'd gone to the river to be alone to think about his life—his father had expected him to take his proper place at the mill, but he hadn't been sure that was what he wanted.

Cara and a bunch of her friends had invaded his solitude. She'd stepped on some glass and cut her foot, a deep gash in the instep. He'd carried her to his car and taken her to the doctor. The cut had needed five stitches to close it.

He remembered she hadn't cried or used the injury as a come-on to him the way other girls might have. He'd liked that.

There'd been lots of things he'd liked about her. The way the laughter would dance in her eyes before it hit her mouth. The quiet way she'd listened to his plans, the trust she'd shown when she'd shared her dreams. Before summer was over, their plans and dreams had merged. That had been before the embezzlement had been discovered.

After that, whatever he and Cara had shared was gone forever. She'd refused to see him because he couldn't in all honesty say that he thought her father was innocent. Dammit, all the circumstances had pointed to the man.

After the case was dropped due to lack of evidence, her family had moved away, and he'd heard no more. She hadn't answered any of the letters he'd sent. He'd vowed to forget her.

Then Miss Josie had mentioned Cara and asked if he remembered her and her family. Without stopping to think of the possible consequences of seeing her

again, he'd written a letter to her in care of her stepfather's company, requesting an evaluation of the furniture he'd inherited. He'd been curious, he admitted....

Footsteps in the hall stopped the flow of memories.
He leaped to his feet, but she entered before he could
go to the door and greet her. She'd changed into red
wool slacks and a print shirt.

A pulse throbbed in his lower body. He stifled it.
The past was dead and buried. Right. But he wasn't.

"Come on in," he invited. "I was just wondering
about you."

Her smile came easily, he noted. She'd gotten over
her qualms about being there. Now if he could control
his impulses...

"I decided to take a nap. Then when I woke, I
couldn't resist the bathroom. I've never taken a
shower like that before."

The bath had an overhead shower in the middle of
the huge tiled room. The bathtub, which had gold
fixtures, occupied one wall, double sinks the other.
Her confession conjured up visions in his mind better
left alone. Cara, letting him touch her... Cara, letting
him kiss her sweet breasts, run his tongue over the
pink nipples... Cara, with her smoky-blue eyes closed
in rapture, her lips parted on a soft moan...

Desire lanced through him, more pain than pleasure. He motioned for her to have a seat and hurried
to the concealed wet bar in the wall. Sending for her
had been a definite mistake. It had been too long since
he'd had time for a woman.

Cara wished she hadn't mentioned the shower. The
darkening of Adam's eyes showed where his thoughts
had led him. His glance ran over her, touching her

skin with a searing glow that had nothing to do with central heat. She was relieved when he abruptly walked away after waving toward a chair.

"The rain has started," he said, his tone oddly harsh.

She followed his gaze. Rain struck the window pane with an icy patter. "I'm glad I'm not out in it."

"What would you like to drink?" he asked.

She murmured, "Nothing, thank you." What had set him off? "Will the rain cause problems for you at the mill?"

His mouth quirked up in a wry smile. "Not any more than usual."

Before Cara could reply to this, Mrs. Groves came to the door. "Dinner is ready," she said. She lingered, her blue eyes lighting on Cara, a warm smile of welcome on her face.

"Mrs. Groves, do you recall Cara Gardner?" Adam asked.

"Indeed, I do. She thought my cookies were the best in the world. Not even her own mother could do better, although she asked me not to tell." The woman's manner was sincere.

"They were," Cara affirmed, returning Mrs. Groves's smile. The housekeeper was the same as always. Her figure was still plump, her manner good-natured. Cara had gone to school with the youngest Groves son, a redhead like his mother.

"Where is Jerry now?" she asked. "Does he live here?"

A momentary worry dashed into Mrs. Groves's blue eyes. "He's in the service, does something on computers for the navy. They sent him to college for it.''

Cara laughed. ''And he told me he wasn't ever going to school again if he got out of Paradise Falls High.''

''Miss Josie's English class nearly did him in,'' his mother agreed, laughing. The two women talked a few more minutes, then Mrs. Groves bustled off to see about the meal. ''Your soup is on the table.''

''Shall we?'' Adam waited for her to join him.

Cara had no choice but to walk beside him for the short distance down the hall to the dining room. She was aware of his body heat against her shoulder when they accidentally brushed each other. She realized she would like to touch him, just run her hands all over him the way a person liked to stroke velvet.

More than that, she wanted him to stroke her the way he used to, his hands large and strong and gentle, oh, so gentle, on her.

A tingling sensation lodged in her chest. Her body seemed to change, becoming heavy with desire.

It would be a dreadful mistake to allow old embers to be stirred between her and Adam. She stepped away from him.

Chapter Two

Two steaming bowls of potato cream soup were on the table when they entered the dining room. A silver basket held assorted crackers. Adam seated her to his right and took his place at the head of the table.

Looking down the elegant cherry table flanked by six chairs on each side, Cara realized if she were hostess she would sit at the other end, far from him when they had guests.

But when the guests departed, the host and hostess would be left alone to recap and share the evening....

"When do you want to start to work?" Adam asked.

She returned to reality. "Monday, if that's all right. I had thought I'd explore the town tomorrow, then have lunch with Sally Winetski at the Asher Inn. She and I were friends in school."

"I know Sally. She's doing very well in her real estate business, it seems."

"So she told me." Cara smiled. Being with Sally

would be relaxing. She'd already spoken to her by phone.

"I can take you for a tour tomorrow," Adam volunteered. "I'll show you the highlights of the town." His smile was sardonic.

She hesitated before accepting his offer. She'd thought to have the time alone, to reacquaint herself with the old hangouts and confront any leftover ghosts. Better to face things alone and get it over with....

A movement from Adam made her glance at him. She thought she saw a flicker of anger in his eyes, then it was gone. "That would be nice," she said, accepting his offer.

"The area has grown in eight years," he told her. "There's a resort going in over the western ridge. We might get a new road that connects to the interstate highway out of it."

"That would be an improvement."

He shrugged. "Some people are for it, some against. You know how it goes in a small town— everyone has an opinion."

He picked up the basket of crackers and held it for her while she made a selection, then he helped himself. When he lifted his spoon, she did the same.

The soup was good, but she hardly tasted it. She was too aware of the man beside her. They spoke of the weather or the town while they ate, and the rain filled the short silences. When she wasn't staring at her plate, she stared at the ornate room.

"Is this worth anything?" he finally asked, waving a hand to indicate the dining room furnishings.

"A lot, I should think. I remember your mother once saying the table, chairs and hutch had originally belonged to Martha Washington. If you have the papers to document it, the set would be valuable.''

"How valuable?"

She perused the contents of the room, then shrugged. "I'm not sure. I'll have to do some checking."

"What would be the best way to sell it?"

Surprise showed in her eyes. "Well, an auction at one of the big houses in New York would get you the most. I think they'd list it, due to its historical value.''

"Could you handle the details?"

"Yes. Are...are you thinking of selling some things?"

"Yes."

His short answer didn't encourage questions. She asked anyway. "But...why?"

"I need the money."

"Oh." Cara couldn't contain her shock. Her mind raced with a multitude of thoughts.

The Clairmonts had been the richest people around for as long as she could remember. Adam's great-great-great-grandfather had purchased the land and started the mill using steam-powered looms shortly after the Civil War.

Paradise Falls had been a typical mill town, every house and store owned and controlled by the Clairmonts until well after the turn of the century. The family had been associated with wealth and held *the* prominent social position in the area for decades.

He laughed grimly. "Don't look so shocked. Everyone needs money. Haven't you heard? It's what makes the world go round."

Mrs. Groves entered with the serving cart. After

removing the bowls, she set their meal before them, each plate artfully arranged with thin slices of rare roast beef and steaming vegetables. A crusty loaf of bread, right out of the oven, accompanied the meal. She looked over the table to make sure she hadn't forgotten anything and left them.

Cara glanced at Adam. The smile at the corners of his mouth was cynical, the expression in his eyes unreadable.

"A cash-flow problem?" she inquired with a twist of amusement to match his.

He sliced the bread and served her before taking a piece for himself. "You could call it that," he admitted while he spread a thin layer of butter over the bread.

Thinking of money brought to mind her suspects. She, her mother and stepfather had settled on two people as the prime candidates. The first was Mr. Wagner, chief accountant at the mill, now retired. He had worked directly under her father, who had been the treasurer. The second suspect was Adam's father.

Cara had thought that idea ridiculous when her stepfather had broached it, until Thomas Townsend had pointed out Mr. Clairmont wouldn't be the first man in history to take money from his own company. She tried to imagine the patrician mill owner paying off gambling debts or blackmail due to a spicy sex scandal. The image wouldn't come.

During her visits to the mansion, Mr. Clairmont had treated her with a grave courtesy she'd never forgotten. She detected elements of that charm in Adam.

She let her gaze linger on him while he ate his dinner, his mind obviously occupied with his own worries. Compassion washed over her as she noticed subtleties about him that had escaped her earlier. The lines about his eyes indicated tension, and his manner toward her had been strained from the moment she'd arrived.

A touch of his earlier cynicism invaded her. Both of them had learned not to expect too much of life. Even Adam Clairmont of Clairmont Textiles wasn't immune to misfortune, it seemed.

"I had wondered..." she began, then stopped.

He looked at her with a question in his eyes.

"I had wondered about the competition from the big companies."

He shrugged. "The wholesale market is world-wide in several industries, but particularly in material and clothing. Americans have got to learn to compete."

"I agree."

With an interested audience, Adam found himself expounding upon ideas he'd kept to himself since he'd taken control of the mill. There were markets out there he wanted to go for. If he could find the money.

He'd never told anyone how stunned he'd been when he'd gone over the books after his father's death. Like everyone in town, he'd thought the mill was solid. It had been chugging along for six generations and would keep going forever.

The facts had exposed the truth. The personal money—a sizable fortune—his father had put into the company had only staved off the inevitable for a few more years.

Adam had cut costs, bargained with his suppliers and finally, reluctantly, laid off workers. The mill was now breaking even. However, there was no extra money for conversion to computer-controlled equipment. Without that, they'd eventually lose out to the bigger mills.

"A Japanese company has made me an offer," he concluded, returning to dismal reality after soaring with his dreams. He'd probably bored her to death with all his lofty philosophy of world marketing schemes.

"You'd sell Clairmont Textiles?" she asked, plainly aghast.

"Would you rather see it closed?" he asked. "Would you prefer that to selling to outsiders? The town will die without some industry to keep it going."

Cara realized he'd reverted to his earlier cynical amusement, but after the past few minutes of discussion, of watching his eyes gleam as he talked of his plans, she knew it was a facade.

He'd had other dreams eight years ago, but he cared about the town and its people. They'd depended on the mill for their livelihood for generations. He wouldn't let them down, whatever he had to do. He'd put aside his dreams in order to save theirs.

A fierce aching rush of sympathy assailed her.

He waved a hand. "Enough of my problems. Tell me of your life. How did you get interested in antiques? If I remember correctly, you wanted to be a psychologist and work with families."

There'd been no money after the embezzlement scandal. Her father, although released, hadn't been able to find a job with another company. He'd opened his own accounting office with the last of their savings, auditing books and advising companies on income tax preparation. They'd all worked after they moved to Virginia—her father, her mother and herself.

"I worked after school in the Townsend warehouse, dusting and cataloging the items. I discovered a certain fascination with old stuff. Each piece had a history and story of its own."

"Based on the families who had owned it," Adam murmured.

"Yes. I learned which families were doing well and which were in a decline, according to whether they were buying or selling." She realized what she was saying and stopped.

He didn't take offense at the implication, but seemed to find the idea amusing. "It looks as if the Clairmonts are definitely in decline, doesn't it?" He paused, then gave her an insouciant grin. "After all, I'm the only one left."

"You can still marry and have children."

"Carrying on the family name isn't high on my agenda." He stood. "Shall we go into the library for coffee? We'll have a fire to drive out the chill."

She was relieved to change the subject. "That would be nice."

The two of them alone, with the wind and rain beating outside the house while they were cozy inside in front of a fire?

Danger.

The warning pounded against her eardrums when they entered the library. She clasped her hands in her lap to hide her state of nerves after she was seated in a comfortable chair.

She couldn't afford to be distracted by Adam and his long-lost dreams, she thought, while he built the fire. Her loyalty was to her family. Her mother was depending on her.

A picture of a hawk in flight, soaring over the valley and looking for its nest, came to her.

She hadn't come back to stay, she reminded herself sternly. She had a job to do and a goal to accomplish. That was all.

Turning to business, she and Adam talked for hours, planning her schedule and the scope of the work she was to do for him.

"Give me a week to straighten things out at the mill before you come down there. I'll alert my secretary to make a duplicate key to the storeroom for you."

"That would be convenient," she said, feeling excited and guilty at the same time. An impulse to confess her ulterior motive in accepting his job offer almost overpowered her common sense.

On dark summer nights, parked on the bluff overlooking the valley, she'd confided all the secrets of her love-struck heart to Adam. But that was long ago.

They fell silent, both staring into the fire. The flames had died to embers, she noted. The clock bonged out ten strokes. She patted back a yawn and finished her cup of coffee.

"You probably would like to go to your room," Adam said, reverting to his role of polite, albeit remote, host.

Cara stood when he did. She saw his gaze move to her lips. It stayed. She knew, with some deeply instinctive knowledge, that he wanted her, that he was thinking of kissing her, of holding her, of making love to her.

She froze, her heart hurting with the force of its

wild dance in her chest. "Yes," she managed to say, ignoring the unspoken desire. "I just realized I've been up since dawn. Mountain air. I'd forgotten how invigorating it can be."

His expression became opaque. He swung around and closed the glass partitions of the fireplace. "Most people do. A mineral spa for the tourists would probably do well here."

Cara sighed. The temptation had been successfully turned aside. If she'd taken just one tiny step forward, would she have ended the night in his arms?

On the way up the stairs, she considered this question and worried about the strange, tense moment just past. She realized there was still a spark between them, an ember that had never quite burned itself out.

A tremor ran over her as a gush of rain hit the window in her room when she entered and closed the door. He had wanted her, yes; but worse, she had wanted him.

Cara awoke with a start. For a moment she was disoriented, wondering why her room was so dark, thinking the streetlight must be out. Then she remembered she was high on the side of the mountain in Adam Clairmont's house and there were no streetlights at all around his home.

A loud noise caused every nerve in her body to jerk. After a rapid *knock, knock, knock,* the racket stopped. Someone at the door? No, the knocking was too uneven for that. When she heard it again, she realized a shutter must have come loose.

Getting up, she pulled her blue robe over her gown, glad of its fleecy warmth, and slipped her feet into scuffs. Another spurt of noise, softer this time, directed her out her door and down the steps. Downstairs, she waited in the dark hall for another clue.

Blam! Blam!

She followed the sound into the kitchen. There, light from the stove clock erased the deep gloom and lent a softer ambiance to the night's shadows. She felt like a ghost, wandering aimlessly on its nightly rounds.

"Don't move," a harsh voice ordered.

Cara froze.

Light flooded the room, and she gave an involuntary shriek. Her captor was Adam...dressed in hastily pulled-on jeans, with the snap and zipper still unfastened.... He clicked the safety on his pistol and lowered the weapon to his side.

"Oh," she said, pressing a hand to her heart.

"What are you doing down here?" His tone held annoyance.

"I heard a noise—"

"So did I. I think a shutter has pulled free."

"That's what I decided." To her own ears, she sounded defensive, as if guilty of some crime. Her eyes slid from his, paused at his bare chest and dropped to the V where his jeans hung open. It was obvious he wore nothing under them. Naturally he would be the type to sleep in the buff. If they slept together...

He laid the gun on the counter and, partially turning his back, pulled the denim closed and clicked the snap into place. She watched, without a thought for modesty, while he closed the zipper. He was still in superb condition.

Heat swept through Cara. It seemed to burn her skin from the inside out. The hiss of a sharply drawn breath brought her eyes to his. He exhaled with an exasperated sound, anger and need burning in the hot depths of his eyes.

With an oath he tucked the gun into his waistband and went into the pantry. Through the open door, she watched as he raised the window and pulled the loose shutter toward him. He worked on the hook, secured it to the catch, gave a tug on it and closed the window. Cold air swirled into the kitchen, giving her a case of chill bumps. She felt like a fever victim, now hot, now cold.

He came back, glanced at her, then the clock. She checked the time. Two a.m.

"You want some hot chocolate?" he asked. It was more a snarl than a polite inquiry. A frown etched a deep vertical line in his forehead. He reminded her of a lone wolf, angry and suspicious of others in his territory.

She shook her head and took a step back.

His gaze stormed over her, producing chills inside as well as outside her, overcoming the feverish excitement of a moment ago. His voice became as icy as a mountain spring. "Look, maybe having you here isn't the best idea I've come up with. God knows I have enough problems without taking on more, but it's done. We have a contract. Can we leave it at that? I'm not going to pounce on you when you least expect it."

His attitude hurt her for some reason. She lifted an insolent eyebrow. "Will you when I most expect it?" From the way his eyes widened, she knew she'd surprised him with the acid barb.

Now he was looking at her through glittering slits, like a predator examining his prey, and she acknowledged this older Adam was much tougher, much harder to handle, than the young man she'd known and loved. A fresh tingle of excitement shot through her, and she had to open her mouth to draw enough air into her lungs.

"So it isn't all one-sided," he murmured, a cynical smile curling his lips. "You feel it, too."

She shrugged. "The past is hard to forget."

"Believe me, I haven't forgotten a moment of it." His voice became deceptively soft...like a growl. "Like how you felt in my arms." His gaze slammed into her like ice shards. "Like how you walked away and never looked back."

In spite of his mocking tone, as if he really didn't care, she absurdly felt guilty for not answering his letters, even though she hadn't believed his confident assurance that they could work things out. After all, *his* family hadn't been slow roasted over the coals of public opinion. "There's such a thing as family loyalty."

"Yes," he agreed. His steady perusal was like needle-sharp teeth gliding over her flesh, leaving her with tiny wounds, open and hurting. Then his attention changed, and she saw desire burn in him. If he reached for her, she wasn't sure how she'd react.

She didn't get a chance to find out.

He stalked to the door. "Turn the light out when you go up." He walked out.

In the echoing silence, she pulled the fleecy warmth of the robe tightly about her. She snapped off the light and went up the steps in the dark, feeling her way. Her goal loomed before her. No matter what her misgivings were—and she definitely sensed disaster closing in—she had to accomplish her task.

* * *

Cara didn't wake up until almost ten the next morning. She dressed and went downstairs with a wariness new to her. Mrs. Groves was in the kitchen. She gave Cara a warm greeting.

"There's warm muffins in the basket. Juice is in that pitcher on the table. Shall I fix you some eggs?"

"Good morning." Cara poured a glass of orange juice. "No eggs, thanks. I usually eat cereal for breakfast."

Mrs. Groves sighed. "Everyone is watching their fat intake these days. I tell you, it almost takes the joy from cooking...no cream in pasta dishes, no fatback to season vegetables, no bacon drippings with corn bread."

Cara laughed, the last of the previous night's tension leaving her. After putting two muffins on a plate and pouring a cup of coffee, she took a seat at the round table next to a window.

"Is it all right if I eat in here?" she asked.

"Of course." Mrs. Groves finished stuffing a roast, wrapped it in foil and put it in the oven at a low temperature. "Adam takes most of his meals at the kitchen table these days. Or in the library. That boy," she muttered and shook her head.

Cara sipped her juice and gazed out at the sunshine. The day was as bright as newly washed sheets. Nature seemed to be apologizing for the lingering nasty weather, or else teasing them before sending more of the same. A walk in the woods would be perfect, she thought, then remembered that Adam had volunteered to drive her around the valley.

Not wanting to think of him, she said, "I didn't think you would be here today. Adam said you'd gone to visit your daughter."

Mrs. Groves poured a cup of coffee and joined her at the table. "I did. Baby-sat for her last night while they went to a movie over in Beckley. But I came home early this morning. Good thing," she said darkly. "Adam would have left you on your own the whole day most likely. He's already in the library, working."

"Oh, I didn't hear him when I came down the hall." The door had been closed, she remembered.

"He works too hard," Mrs. Groves confided in a lowered voice. "I was hoping that while you were here, you could lure him into having some fun. It's not natural for a young man his age to spend all his time worrying about that mill."

"But I'm here to work, too."

Mrs. Groves waved that notion aside. "Adam needs you."

Cara's hand jerked as that statement registered, and she slopped juice on the table. She wiped it up with her napkin. "He needs me to inventory his house, yes—"

"And to bring some light into his life."

"I'm not the little match girl," Cara said, keeping her tone amused despite the restless flicker of emotion along her nerves.

Mrs. Groves silently contemplated the peak on the far side of the valley. "I know about you and Adam."

Cara set her cup down with a clatter. "I beg your pardon?"

"His mother was a big one for keeping pictures of all the parties here at the house. Adam took the ones of you and made up an album one summer, starting from the time you came here for your first Christmas party when you were just a toddler, hardly bigger than a minute and into everything.''

"I'm sure he's forgotten all that by now," Cara murmured.

Mrs. Groves was in a nostalgic mood. She continued, "That same summer he started sleeping with his shirt spread over his pillow. I thought it was odd until I realized the shirt smelled of perfume." She turned her bright blue gaze to Cara. "I wondered who the girl was who'd finally stolen his heart. When I saw you two walking through the woods near here one day, I knew."

The dead certainty in Mrs. Groves's voice prevented Cara from speaking the denial that sprang to her tongue. "It was a summer romance," she said instead, "a temporary thing."

Mrs. Groves narrowed her eyes and gave Cara a significant perusal. "I'd hoped, with your coming here and all, that he'd remember there was a world outside Clairmont Textiles. You could help him."

Cara could only stare at Mrs. Groves in astonishment. Her help Adam? It was the most ridiculous suggestion she'd ever heard. "He doesn't need my help. Except for the work I'm going to do."

The housekeeper sighed, her disappointment in Cara plain. "He gave up his law office in order to take over the mill when his father had his first spell of illness."

"I remember," Cara said. The newspaper article about Clayton Clairmont's illness and death had made a hero of Adam for giving up his life in Wheeling to stay in Paradise Falls and save the mill and the town that depended on it.

"I worry about him. I've watched him grow from

a boy into a fine man. It's not right that he have all the burdens of life and none of the rewards.'' With that, Mrs. Groves got up, rinsed out her cup and resumed her work.

Cara finished her breakfast, her sympathy for Adam growing in spite of her admonitions that his problems weren't hers. She couldn't afford to become entangled in his life. She knew that, yet here she was feeling sorry for him, and she hadn't been in town twenty-four hours.

Before she could sort out her reactions, Adam came into the kitchen. "Any more coffee, Mrs. G.?'' he asked. He saw Cara. His smile faded. When it returned, she saw that it had changed.

Cara ignored the stab of remorse at seeing the curtain of polite host descend over his eyes. She disregarded the thought that he'd been as hurt by their breakup as she had been. He'd been angry, but that was all. Look how cynical he'd been last night.

Besides, after eight years he certainly wouldn't still be mourning the loss of their romantic interlude. It wouldn't have lasted, anyway. He'd surely have fallen for one of those brilliant women he met in law school. So why hadn't he?

"Good morning,'' he said, nodding in her direction before pouring another cup of coffee in his mug. He came over to the table and sat down.

"Good morning.''

"Are you ready for a quick tour of our growing metropolis?''

"Yes.''

"Which of our famous sights would you like to see first?''

"Well, I thought I'd particularly like the skyscrapers,'' she said, trying for a jot of humor in spite of his sardonic attitude.

He laughed—a quiet, short burst of sound, but still, a laugh.

Cara saw Mrs. Groves smile approvingly at her over Adam's shoulder. She looked away, a flush warming her face.

Adam stood and pushed the chair in. ''Meet me in the front hall in, say, fifteen minutes?''

''Yes, that will be fine.''

She went to her room to freshen up, gathered her purse and warm coat in case the sunshine proved fickle and returned to the hall. The library door was open, and Adam was on the phone. She saw him straighten the papers on his desk and heard his laughter in reply to something his caller said. In a minute he hung up. ''That was Sally. She said if I'd drop you off at the Asher Inn, she'd bring you home. I told her that was fine. Ready?''

''Yes.''

He picked up a fleece-lined jacket, checked that he had his keys and joined her in the hall. ''We'll take the Porsche.''

She realized she'd never ridden in it. ''I hope you're not one of those wild drivers who takes the curves at max speed.''

He paused with his hand on the door. His gaze ran down her like an avalanche. ''No, I take curves slow...real slow.''

Cara grimaced. ''I guess I left myself open for that one.''

''Wide open,'' he agreed.

She looked up, her eyes meeting his. For a second, something shimmered between them, something bright and yearning. For no good reason she laughed, nervous and confused.

"Come on," he invited, sweeping her outside into the crisp air and helping her into the low sports car. In a minute they were off down the winding drive, at a controlled speed that was miles faster than she would have driven it. But she felt safe.

Adam drove her through the town and pointed out the changes, many of which she'd noticed the day before when she'd arrived. He showed her where new houses were going in. "Half-acre estates, the developers are calling them," he explained, then took her to a point on the western ridge to see where the new resort was going in.

"Will the resort be for summer activity only?" she asked.

"You'll have to ask Sally. I don't know much about it."

Cara made a mental note to do so. Any information might afford a clue, especially if it involved a lot of money, such as developing a resort. Sally might know who was in on the deal.

A wisp of gloom swirled around her like fog drifting into the valley. Later, she promised. She would think about her goals later. Right now she wanted to enjoy the day. She stole a glance at Adam as he concentrated on the road. Careful, she warned herself.

Adam circled around the mountain peak on a road she didn't know, coming out near Vista Point on the glacier-cut ridge. He stopped and switched off the engine.

"Remember the story of *Brigadoon?*" he asked.

"Yes."

"Sometimes I stop here and think that Paradise

Falls will disappear into the mist one day—" his voice grew husky "—and I'll be left alone on this ridge, knowing it'll be a hundred years before it appears again and that I'll never get back."

"Would you rather stay or disappear with it?"

He swung around and looked directly at her. "That depends."

"On what?"

"Whether I was alone or with someone."

Wild speculation rushed through her. Her heart beat hard and painfully in her chest. "Is there someone... in town...you'd want to be with?" She was pleased at the lightness of her tone.

"No," he said, his gaze on her mouth. "Not now."

She wasn't sure what he was implying, if anything, but she was suddenly aware of the sunlight falling on her hair and the side of her face like a benediction, of the crystal clarity of the air, of the special way it had felt all those years ago to wake up each morning in love.

Chapter Three

"Mother is still trying to marry me off," Sally complained with a good-natured grin, catching Cara up on the final chapter in her life. "But I'm a tycoon at heart."

Cara found herself laughing in delight at Sally's droll humor and wry remarks. Her friend had matured, but not so much that Cara couldn't recognize her.

Sally was tall—five-nine—and slender of carriage, but she had her mother's full bustline. She'd learned to dress in the conservative clothing of a successful businesswoman rather than the defiantly ragged jeans of her youth, but her warmth and quick wit were the same.

"Mom and Dad are over at Linda's today for Sunday dinner," Sally continued. "I had some work to do at the office and couldn't get off. Linda's pregnant again."

Cara wondered if Sally avoided family gatherings

because of her mother's admonitions about being an old maid. "That will make four children," Cara mused. "Linda always loved babies."

Sally smiled. "I have to admit they have their endearing moments...mostly when they're asleep."

"Right," Cara agreed. She'd never been around many babies, but the few times she'd baby-sat she'd found the children fun and interesting. She and Adam had wanted at least two kids, maybe three or four. Both of them had grown up alone. They'd felt they'd missed something in not having brothers and sisters.

"So, are you involved with anyone?" Sally asked.

Startled by the question, Cara shook her head. "Are you?"

"No. There're only two men in town taller than I am—the police chief and Adam. The chief is overweight and fortyish. That leaves Adam. Since he never comes into the real estate office, how is he going to discover me and fall madly in love?"

"You...*like* Adam Clairmont?" The thought made Cara uneasy.

"Don't look so surprised. A mouse can gaze with longing at a prince, can't she? I've had dreams of him since I was twelve."

"You never told me."

"What was to tell?" Sally lifted her hands and let them fall. Her gaze became serious. "I feel sorry for Adam."

"Sorry?"

"Did you ever think what it must be like to be the chief employer in town?"

Cara shook her head.

"It's life in a gilded cage. He dates a female one time, and the town gossips are speculating the next morning about wedding bells and babies, not necessarily in that order. Ergo, he doesn't date anyone that I know of.''

Cara noted Sally didn't mention Cara's summer romance with Adam and was grateful for her friend's reticence. Or maybe no one had thought it important enough for serious consideration except herself. And Adam. He had been serious…at the time.

The waitress came over to refill their cups.

Sally spoke to her. ''This weather has been an insult to spring, hasn't it? Maybe it's over and spring is really here.''

The waitress advised them more rain was coming, before clearing their table and leaving. The inn was almost empty.

Cara glanced at her watch. It was nearly four. ''I never thought of Adam's life like that,'' she said slowly, still thinking of Sally's terse description.

Sally added a squeeze of lemon and a teaspoon of sugar to her cup of hot tea. ''Sometimes I think he must be the loneliest person in town.''

Cara swallowed a gulp of coffee. It burned all the way down. ''Why…why do you think that? I mean, *Adam Clairmont?*''

''Yeah, I know. He could have his pick of a different woman every night if he wanted to, but…'' Sally shrugged to indicate he didn't.

''He said last night that he was the last of his family,'' Cara mused aloud. ''That the Clairmonts were dying out.''

''Isn't that terrible?'' Sally was sympathetic. ''My family drives me nuts sometimes—you should have seen my mother the last time I took a male home to dinner. She practically served me to him with the soup!''

They laughed at this slightly exaggerated description.

"Anyway, I'd rather have my mom and dad, Linda and Wayne and all their kids, plus the zillion aunts, uncles and cousins—who feel quite free to offer advice on any subject—than to have no one. Can you imagine what that big house must be like for Adam?''

"I...I hadn't thought about that," Cara admitted, seeing a different side to being a Clairmont.

An attack of conscience hit her. She felt like a sneak thief, snooping around in Adam's life. For a moment she relived that terrible sensation of being torn apart—caught between loyalty to her family and her sense of betrayal of Adam. But that was eight years ago. This was now.

"He comes home to a *housekeeper*, for heaven's sake," Sally went on. "There're all those rooms and not a soul to snuggle up with on a cold winter's night and play tickle games.''

"Sally!"

Sally ignored the exclamation. "Adam never had a chance. It was a given that he would take over the mill when the time came.''

"Why do you say that?" Cara asked. "He had his own law office in Wheeling.''

"Yes, but family obligation, you know," Sally reminded her. "His bid for freedom had barely started when he had to come home and help his father. Adam stepped in and found a can of worms.''

Cara raised her eyebrows at this sweeping statement.

"The company," Sally continued in a lowered tone.

"Hard times?" Cara questioned cautiously. She didn't know how much the residents knew of the mill's problems and didn't want to betray Adam's confidences of the previous night.

"Right. It strikes me as noteworthy that he's decided to have the family antiques checked over. He's asked me to give him an estimate on the house."

Cara murmured, "Oh."

"This is too close in timing to be coincidental," Sally concluded. "Has he said why he wants the furniture appraised?"

"He's thinking of selling some pieces."

Sally pursed her lips. "I knew all wasn't well at Camelot, but I didn't realize Prince Charming had to sell the throne and the castle, too. Old Clayton must be turning over in his grave."

"Adam hasn't decided what he wants to get rid of. That's my department. After I list and evaluate everything, I'll give him advice on what will move the fastest and bring the best price."

Sally was silent for a long minute. "It's so strange, to think that Clairmonts might not always be the movers and shakers in this town. From some things Dad has mentioned, the company needs to modernize. Although," she added loyally, "Adam has turned things around in the past three years. One of the payroll clerks said he didn't even draw a salary. Everyone knows he's putting every penny back into the mill."

"Maybe things will work out for him."

"I hope so," Sally said. "Have you been through the old hotel yet? Adam was instrumental in getting the town fathers to buy the building, renovate it and rent out the space for stores and offices. After it was a success, Mr. Wagner bought it. The city built a new library wing with the profit."

"Mr. Wagner," Cara echoed the name.

"Yes. He's donated a building to the Historical Society, too. Local history is the big item in town. Adam belongs to the group, although he rarely comes to any meetings. I'm a member and so are most of the merchants. Miss Josie and Mr. Wagner are compiling a book on the founding and settling of the county."

A frisson rushed over Cara. Mr. Wagner seemed to have a lot of money to spend for a retired person on a fixed income. Perhaps he had invested wisely...or perhaps he'd taken money from the mill while he was chief accountant under her father.

"So what do you think of the sweeping changes since you were last here? Are you impressed with our progress?" Sally demanded with a sardonic smile.

They talked of the town and classmates for the rest of the afternoon. It was late when they rose to leave.

"I want to walk back to the house. I'd better start before it gets too dark." Cara pulled her coat on and slung her purse strap over her shoulder.

"That's a mile climb. I'll drive you up."

"No, thanks, I need the exercise. Let's get together for lunch one day this week."

"Okay. Will Wednesday suit your schedule?"

"Yes."

Sally waved goodbye from the porch, obviously not sure she should let her friend hike up the steep road to the big house. At the corner Cara waved a last time and hurried on. At the next corner, instead of going straight, she turned left and walked to the last house on the block.

The house wasn't as big as she remembered, but she had been prepared for that. After all, she wasn't a child anymore. Perspective was different from an adult point of view. Otherwise it looked the same, a neat brick house with dark green shutters and a rust-red front door. Two dormer windows angled out from the roof. The one on the upper right had been in her room.

She studied it for a minute, then walked on past the end of the sidewalk and onto a faint path into the woods. She had no problem finding the rocky out-cropping over a narrow gully that had served as play-house, pirate ship, jungle tree house and whatever else she and Sally had dreamed up. She spied a soda can and a broken doll's dish. Someone still used it. She was glad.

The flat rock at the edge of the drop-off beckoned, and she crossed the tiny meadow and sat down with her legs drawn up to her chest. She rested her head on her knees.

Surely if Mr. Wagner had taken that money, he'd have moved away. Instead, she had discovered from Sally that he lived in the same house he'd bought years ago, expecting to be married. His fiancée had died, hit by lightning in a freak storm while out on a picnic with friends.

Life could be unbearably cruel, she mused. If she found he was the guilty one, his life would be torn apart. Just as her family's had been, she reminded herself. She mustn't be such a bleeding heart for other people.

Of course the thief could be someone they hadn't even thought of. Perhaps Mr. Clairmont's secretary.

She had retired and moved to Texas or someplace out west shortly before the scandal broke.

Another thought intruded. If Adam was having money troubles, could the embezzler be at work again? That would mean he or she was still at the mill. If she found the culprit, the discovery would help Adam.

Motive and opportunity. That's what her stepfather had said she must look for. Motive and opportunity. And some hard proof to show to the judge and reopen the case.

She closed her eyes and pressed her forehead against her knees. What if she failed? Or succeeded and hurt a lot of other people? Sometimes, she thought, it might be better to let the past go. But she had promised her mother she'd try.

If Adam's father had done it, Adam would be hurt....

Leaping to her feet, she started on the path up the hill. Her cheeks were flushed and her legs in pain by the time she slammed the front door against the wind, which was howling like a fury down the gorge. The sun had disappeared behind a cloud.

Adam threw the report on his desk and stared into space. He didn't feel like working. Instead of the fine print of the contract, he kept seeing firelight sparkling off a cloud of shiny dark hair and a face that had a natural glow like...he could only think of peaches or roses. A trite comparison to the real thing.

Lifting his coffee mug, he found it was empty. Irritated, he strode over to the coffeemaker and poured another cup.

Instead of returning to his desk and getting his

mind back on his work, he stood by the window and stared out at the late Sunday afternoon landscape. The wind was howling again, blowing down the mountainside as if it wanted to dislodge the town from its protective groove and sling it to hell and beyond.

"Damn," he muttered, stomping across the room.

He flung the contract into a drawer and locked his desk. Grabbing a jacket, he pulled it on over his sweat suit and rammed an old hat on his head. Locking the front door behind him, he pulled on gloves. He drove home, but his frustration and anger needed release. At a comfortable pace, he struck out on foot through the woods, the peace and exertion relaxing him. Calmer, he headed back to the house.

What was Cara doing? he wondered, his breath labored as he struggled up the last steep section. Probably relaxing in front of the fire. Or maybe she was one of those go-getters who started to work immediately. Maybe she already had half the furniture listed and priced.

He balked at thinking of money. He was sick of it.

What he really wanted, he realized when he reached his house, was a woman waiting inside for him, a willing—make that *eager*—woman, one who would welcome his embrace and return it.

He remembered burying his hands in a mass of rich, dark hair and holding Cara's face still, while he kissed her all over. She'd been eager for his touch...at one time.

His body was taut and aching by the time he let himself in the back door. He stopped at the kitchen sink and drank a large glass of water, then blotted the sweat that trickled into his eyes with his sleeve.

A note from Mrs. G., stuck to the refrigerator door,

informed him she'd gone to her daughter's house. Her grandson was ill, and her daughter had asked her to come.

That probably meant he and Cara would be alone in the house tonight...again. He swore softly. The tension between the two of them was ridiculous. Well, there was no help for it. Perhaps the inventory wouldn't take long. Then she'd be gone.

For a second he allowed himself to think of how things might have been. If they'd been married for a couple of years, she would be waiting for him in the master suite. Would she mind if he kissed her while he was sweaty? Would she mind if he made love to her? He closed his eyes as a shudder racked through him.

She would smell wonderful—sweetly perfumed yet with the faint aroma of pure, mysterious woman.

He looked down at the front of his sweatpants. Great. Keep thinking like that and he'd make a fool of himself when she walked into the house.

Mocking laughter rang in his mind. He'd made a fool of himself for her once, laying his dreams at her feet. Never again would he let himself be that trusting, that vulnerable to another person.

He jogged down the hall and into his room. Shedding his clothes as he crossed the carpeted floor, he headed for the shower, pausing on the way to dial Cara's room. No answer.

Ruthlessly he acknowledged a thought that had troubled him since she'd accepted the job. Why had she returned to Paradise Falls? It obviously bothered her, so why was she here?

Thirty minutes later, all the sweat washed away, his hair dry and his restless body restrained in gray flannel slacks and a red and black flannel shirt, he was in the kitchen again, peering into the oven at a casserole. Mrs. G. had prepared it earlier and left him instructions on heating it for supper.

He walked to the window. The woods were dark with menacing shadows. The faint lights of town gleamed through the tossing pine trees. Picking up the phone, he tried Cara's intercom line again. Still no answer. Where the hell was she?

With a grimace, he reminded himself that she didn't have to report in to him. She and Sally were probably talking up a storm, the way women did even if it had only been eight hours rather than eight years since they'd last met.

He glanced at the clock. After six. He would wait until seven, then...then he'd eat. The front door opened.

"Hello?"

"Hello," he called back, going to meet her. He realized his heart was beating abnormally fast, that his voice was husky and rough with a passion he couldn't control. It was going to be another long night.

Cara felt her coat being lifted from her shoulders. She let Adam take it from her and hang it in the closet. When he faced her, his expression was grim.

"What did you do this afternoon?" she asked without stopping to consider the intimate demand in the question.

"Worked."

"Don't you ever take a day off?"

"No."

He was being deliberately short with her, and she felt out of place, an interloper. Had she imagined the warmth of his hello? She paused at the steps, wondering if she should go to her room.

He glanced at her. "There's a fire in the library."

She followed him into the room. He poured two glasses of white wine without asking her preference. "There's a chicken casserole for dinner," he said.

His glance took her in, weighing and measuring each inch until her blood sang hotly in her veins. It was the way he used to look at her. Just before he kissed her.

"That sounds good," she replied, taking the glass.

The wind sighed over the house, piping an eerie note around the eaves before sliding down into the valley toward the town. It sounded mournful, as if it had lost something close to its heart.

"I didn't hear a car. Didn't Sally bring you home?"

Cara shook her head. "I wanted to walk."

"And think," he added as if he could read her mind.

"Yes." She looked out the window. "Have you listened to the news? Are we in for more rain and sleet like last night?"

"There's another storm front on the way." He took a sip of wine. "Mrs. G. will probably spend the night at her daughter's house again."

"Oh, she isn't here?" A quiver invaded her voice. "No."

The conversation lagged. Adam seemed hard-edged tonight. Had she provoked his anger? They'd parted on good terms at the inn. She considered their morning tour. Yes, all had gone well.

They prepared trays and ate dinner in the library in front of the fire. Conversation was as fitful as the moaning of the wind. Adam insisted on taking care of the dishes when they finished.

Cara snuggled deeper into the comfortable chair. She could go to sleep without any effort, sitting there warm and cozy in front of the fire, not letting herself think.

"Are you asleep?" Adam asked, returning with two cups of coffee. She noted he avoided looking directly at her while he placed her cup on the table.

"No, but I could drift off," she admitted. "The storm has brought the rain again. It's comforting to be inside when the elements outside turn nasty."

"People will be setting out their gardens soon. The rain will help loosen the ground."

"I remember. We used to have a garden when we lived here."

"Did you go by your old house today?"

She slipped her shoes off, pulled her feet under her, and turned sideways in the wing chair. "Yes," she said when she was sure her voice was steady.

"The people who own it, the Masons, work at the mill, both husband and wife. They have a daughter, about ten, I think."

"Umm," she said, not wanting to talk. It was easier to drift. Tomorrow her job would start. Then she would think.

Adam added another log to the fire. The clock on the mantel softly chimed the hour. Eight o'clock. Not late.

Much too late, she corrected. Too late for any of the things she was feeling toward Adam. Such as warm. Such as soft.

Since that morning, when he'd put himself out to be charming and entertaining, she'd fought her basic instincts. Earlier they'd burned bright and clear in her, now they were lazily glowing, ready to be stoked to life.

"You've grown into a woman more beautiful than I could ever have imagined," he said. A wry smile twisted his mouth. "And I've imagined a lot."

She roused from her dreamy state, instantly alert, scenting danger in the intimate quiet. The beat of the rain, the crackling of the fire were the only sounds for a long minute. Then she managed to laugh. "So have I."

A log split in the fireplace, its pieces falling off the grate. Adam pushed them back into place with the poker. When he finished, he turned to face her, still kneeling on the hearth. The fire backlighted his shoulders and head, producing a golden aura around him. She wanted to touch him.

My dream prince. My first love.

Yearning gathered deep inside her. For so long her life had been circumscribed by school and work, by her staunch support of her family through their difficult years, then by her concern for her widowed mother. She'd rarely dated. There hadn't been time.

Now, all that she'd missed, all that she'd lost, surged before her, tempting her to reach out and take what she wanted.

Carefully, aware of the fragility of her own control, she set her cup back on its saucer. "I think I'll go up and read."

Adam saw fear leap into her eyes and wondered if his foolish confession had caused it. He remembered how his body had reacted when he saw her climb out of her van and come toward him across the parking lot at the mill.

Raw, primitive need, that's what he'd felt. He felt it now. It was darned embarrassing to be at the mercy of his libido.

"Scared?" he asked and immediately regretted it. Stupid.

She didn't pretend to misunderstand. "Of being alone with you? No."

"The night isn't over yet." He smiled, feeling the grim march of slow hour after slow hour and the frustrating buildup of desire. "Don't trust me, Cara. You don't know me like you think you do. I'm not the idealist I once was."

He didn't know why he was warning her, except he didn't quite trust himself around her. He hadn't found a level place in regard to her and their past. It kept getting mixed up with the present.

It was almost funny—how ambiguous he felt toward her. Some part of him thought she should be his. Another part urged caution. He'd learned not to take life at face value.

He returned to his chair before she noted his arousal. Uneasy currents flowed between them.

"Nor am I," she said.

He nodded. "We've both had a few lessons in the school of hard knocks, haven't we?"

Hers had been the hardest, he admitted. Passion and sympathy condensed into a need to hold her. Once she'd gone to him for comfort, for assurance of his belief in her father's innocence. He hadn't been able to give it then; he couldn't now.

"We both survived." Cara didn't understand his mood nor the tinge of bitterness she detected in him. But the simmer of desire, controlled and powerful, was visible in his eyes. That was the one thing they'd never hidden from each other.

She stood, aware that she should leave at once. He did the same. They were no more than two feet apart—one step for each of them, one reach of the arms.

"Damn," he muttered, the word harsh, angry.

His name was an ache in her throat. It parted her lips and slipped into the night air with the muted softness of a newborn's first cry. In the end, it was Adam who made the first move.

She found herself in his arms, crushed as close as possible to his chest. He didn't kiss her as she had expected, but simply held her, his cheek against her hair, his lips pressing delicate impressions along her temple.

"You always made me think of new-mown grass," he said in a tone rough with need. "The freshness of morning was in your scent, and your taste...it reminded me of summer fruit."

Cara felt his lips move against her hair.

"Tart," he continued, "but with a hint of the sweetness that would ripen in you with maturity."

Lifting her head, she leaned back against his embrace to look at him, knowing she was inviting his kiss. Adam let his gaze roam over her face before hungrily focusing on her mouth.

Her lips trembled and stilled as he came to her. His mouth descended slowly, as if he fought a will stronger than his.

She managed to turn her head. "This is wrong," she whispered.

"Why?" he demanded, his mouth glancing along her jaw, leaving burning caresses.

"It's...we're remembering the past." She wedged her hands between their pounding hearts.

"The past be damned."

"Adam," she whispered, a plea for sanity. Liquid fire seemed to be spreading through her veins, making her pliable and yielding. Another moment and she would forget her goals and melt in his arms. "Don't. You're my enemy."

He jerked back as if she'd struck him. "What did you say?"

When he dropped his arms from her, she felt the coldness rush in and enclose her. She turned away, needing to escape the fury in his eyes. His hand on her arm stopped her flight.

"What did you say?" he asked again, his tone harder.

She faced him. "I didn't mean that, not exactly."

"What exactly did you mean?" All expression had left his face. It could have been a mask cast in bronze. The light of the fire flickered across his cheekbones, making him appear as remote as a pagan god and as merciless.

A tremor ran through her. "Nothing."

"The hell you didn't." When she protested, he interrupted with a contemptuous curl of his lip, "*Enemy?* A woman doesn't issue invitations like the one you just gave me to someone she hates. Unless she wants something." His eyes narrowed.

"I don't," she gasped, stunned.

He caught her shoulders and pulled her close. "Like hell. Since the moment you arrived, I've seen the questions in your eyes. You were curious about us. Were you wondering if you could still make me wild with need for you?"

His hands slipped behind her, down her back to her hips. He brought her into contact with his body.

"Did you ever doubt it?" he ground out.

Heat unfurled inside her. She pressed her hands against him, acutely aware of the feel of him where they touched. He was like wildfire, and he ignited desires she'd suppressed long ago.

Before she could move, his hands came to her face and captured it. He held her captive while his mouth took hers.

The kiss wasn't gentle. It was harsh with his own needs, male needs that sought and demanded an answer from her. She couldn't help but respond. All the longing she'd hidden deep inside surged forth, reminding her that she was a woman. She knew beyond a doubt that he was all man.

His tongue stroked her lips, and when she parted them, he took possession of her mouth. He'd taught her to kiss like this. But she wasn't a naive teenager anymore. The kiss was full of passion, but there was no tenderness in it.

She clutched his shirt and held on until the tactile assault ended as abruptly as it began. He pivoted from her and stood in front of the fire, blocking its warmth from her body. He rested his arms on the mantel and stared into the flames.

"Don't tempt me beyond control," he advised without looking at her. "You were too young before, but you're not now."

Frissons of passion danced along her nerves. "Why would I want to...tempt you?" She slowly came back to earth as his distrust penetrated the fog of desire clouding her mind.

"Revenge," he said. His gaze burnt a hole right through her composure. "For what happened between us all those years ago."

Chapter Four

Every nerve in her body tightened, causing her to give a visible start. She lifted a hand and toyed with the gold chain she wore. Recognizing the nervous habit, she dropped her hands to her sides and faced Adam's accusing stare. She wondered what he knew or had guessed. And how she was going to answer.

"That's it, isn't it?" He studied her with a thoroughness that made her heart pound like a frightened fawn's.

"Revenge?" she repeated, stalling while she recouped her poise. "That's ridiculous."

"Is it?"

He pivoted and came toward her. She instinctively took a step backward and felt the chair against her legs.

Stopping only a couple of feet away, he spoke again. "You've never forgiven me for what you saw as a betrayal, but it was you who turned your back on me, not the other way around."

"I didn't!"

"How else would you describe it? You refused to have anything to do with me even after your father was released. You wanted me to deny my doubts and trust your instincts. Well, sorry, I had to deal with the facts as they were. Now, here you are, using the magic you always wove around me, luring me back into the memories of those wild, sweet days.... Did you want to see if you had the same power over me that you had at eighteen?"

Cara shook her head, mesmerized by the fire blazing in his eyes as they swept over her in one burning, caressing glance.

"So now you know," he conceded. "You do." His voice dropped to a husky, barely audible level. "Damn you, you do."

A tortured expression—of self-loathing, she thought—passed over his face. With an oath he walked out of the room. She heard a distant door slam a few seconds later.

Shaking, she sank into the chair and wondered if she should pack and get out. Now...before things grew worse between them.

Adam hadn't realized her true reason for being there. He thought she only wanted some kind of childish revenge on him for not taking her side. But he was suspicious. If he came upon the truth, would he help or hinder her?

If only it were possible to keep emotions out of this. An ache of sorrow and regret settled in her. She rose and made her way upstairs to spend the rest of the evening alone.

On Monday morning Cara dressed in tan slacks and a sweater of deep gold, her favorite color. Her mood needed brightening.

To her shock, Adam was in the kitchen when she went down. "Cereal, eggs, pancakes?" he inquired without any other form of greeting. His face looked as if it had been carved from the hardest West Virginia rock available.

"Cereal." She grimaced. He was playing the lord of the manor this morning—remote, impersonal and cuttingly polite. She would be the same.

"Help yourself." He pointed out the pantry and showed her where the dishes were stored. "Milk is in the refrigerator."

She prepared the cereal, poured a cup of coffee and sat at the table. The day was overcast. She could feel the cold seeping through the window. She barely glanced at Adam when he took the chair opposite, but a glance was all she needed.

In a dark gray business suit, he looked like any successful executive, but there the resemblance stopped. Muted, but not concealed, was an undercurrent of raw anger.

She suppressed the sudden desire to goad him out of his loftier-than-thou attitude. "Do you have any records on the furniture?" she asked. "Old receipts or anything?"

"I haven't had time to look. You can check the desk and file cabinets in the library."

"All right." A beat of excitement went through her. Maybe she would have access to Clayton Clairmont's personal records.

"If you need anything, you can call the mill on the intercom. Dial ten."

"Yes, I remember."

"If I'm not in, my secretary can probably help."

"Thank you." If he were any colder, she'd get frostbite. She wished he'd go.

"If you're finished, I'll show you the files. Bring your cup with you."

"Thank you," she said with a saccharine smile at his back.

He caught the smile and gave her a dark glance before leading the way out of the kitchen.

During the night she'd decided she had to stop acting like a fox caught in the henhouse with a chicken between its teeth. She was going to do the job Adam had hired her to do. Anything else, well, that was her business.

She entered the library. It wasn't until he stopped in front of the files that she realized she was practically treading on his heels. Stepping aside, with a discreet space between them, she looked at him expectantly.

After opening the top drawer, he flicked through the tabs on the folders until he came to the *F*s. "I don't see anything that says furniture," he remarked. He checked his watch. "I have a meeting in a half hour. Mrs. G. hasn't called, so I don't know if she'll be back today. Call me at five and I'll pick up something for dinner before I come home."

"That's okay. I'll just have a salad or a sandwich. You don't have to worry about me."

Adam jerked around to face her. "Look. Maybe this was a crazy idea, having you here. I don't know, and frankly, I don't give a damn—"

"Rhett Butler," she muttered.

"What?"

"Nothing."

"Don't give me that. What the hell did you say?" He pushed back his jacket and hooked both hands on his hips.

She realized they were on the brink of an all-out quarrel. "I'm sorry. I was being a smart-mouth," she confessed. "Rhett Butler said, 'Frankly, my dear, I don't give a damn,' and you said 'Frankly—'"

"I know what I said."

Cara touched one ear as if her hearing had been impaired. "The king of the jungle speaks."

Adam looked as if he might snap her into two pieces with one bite, but when he spoke, he'd lowered his voice. "The bottom drawer is personal junk," he informed her, kicking a toe against the mentioned file drawer.

"Does that mean it's off limits?" She didn't know why she was baiting him. He'd insulted her with the implication that she'd used Lolita tactics on him the previous night—as if she alone were responsible for that ill-advised kiss—but perhaps she'd better placate the beast. "I promise not to bother your...junk."

He gazed at her another moment, nodded and walked out. When he'd gone down the driveway in the Porsche, she breathed easily once more. During the night she'd thought over their wild kiss and had come to some conclusions. If Adam got too close to the truth about her being there, perhaps she could divert him.

Her conscience bothered her on that score. She'd never been the type to use another person's passion for personal reasons. It seemed underhanded and dishonorable. But no more dishonorable than the person who'd taken that money and let her father live under a cloud the rest of his life. Anyway, she had a job to do for Adam, and she'd better get on with it.

She looked through the first three drawers of the file cabinet to no avail. No records in there. She paused at the fourth one, her hand on the handle. The angel and devil—her mother had told her they resided on her shoulders—fought a battle. The angel won... this time. She went to the desk. Nothing there.

Taking a tablet and pencil, she trudged upstairs and started with the first bedroom on the left side. By noon she had two bedrooms done, her list containing all the items in the rooms, including pictures and objets d'art as well as furniture.

She went down and ate a quiet lunch, while gazing out the window at the clouds swirling around the mountain peaks. Mrs. Groves hadn't come back yet, and Cara wondered if Adam had told his housekeeper to stay away. She immediately dismissed that idea. Adam wasn't interested in being alone with her.

After eating, she resumed her task. At five, she quit.

The house was eerily silent as she went to her room. For a second she thought of all the nights Adam must have spent alone in this solitary mansion. *The loneliest man in town.* Perhaps Sally had been right.

She felt grungy after a day of searching over furniture for maker's marks. Even a good housekeeper like Mrs. Groves couldn't keep dust out of every little nook and cranny.

In her room she stripped and then showered. Later she dressed in a warm-up suit of deep blue with a hint of lilac, and sat before the mirror, brushing her hair.

Her eyes, a solemn smoky blue like her mother's, with the same dark lashes and eyebrows that friends had compared to a movie star's, stared back at her, waiflike. She listened to the wind blow around the house and felt a vast loneliness open in her. She didn't like being alone.

She wondered if Adam would bring the food as he'd promised that morning. Should she call him and tell him the housekeeper hadn't returned yet? She decided to check for sure. After laying the brush aside, she pulled on thick socks and went downstairs. No one was in the kitchen or in the quarters beyond it.

"Mrs. Groves?" she called.

Only the mournful sigh of the wind answered her. She went into the library. Six o'clock. She would wait half an hour, then find something to eat. Perhaps she'd go to bed early and read.

Feeling like the heroine in a gothic story, she built a fire and snuggled into an easy chair. The chair was covered in a warm shade of brown, surprisingly homey for the big house. It was also very comfortable. She yawned.

After finding the lever, she put the chair in a semireclining position. From that angle, through the tall, narrow windows, she could look out at the deepening twilight over the mountain ridge above the house. The moon was already visible, a sliver of frosty white like an icicle in the sky.

An hour later she heard Adam's arrival.

He came in through the side door that led to the garage. She heard him call his housekeeper's name just as she'd done earlier. She supposed she'd better sit up. After yawning and stretching, she flipped the lever and the recliner reverted to a rocker.

"Good evening," Adam said.

She spun around in the chair, knocking over the inlaid rosewood and oak table.

Adam strode across the room, lifted the table and righted it. "Sorry. I didn't mean to startle you." He was still in his king-of-the-mountain mode—cool and remote.

"I didn't hear you approaching," she said. Her heart beat like a flushed quail as she gazed at him. Adam at twenty-one had been a dream; at twenty-nine, he was devastating.

He could be imperious, perhaps even arrogant at times, but the powerful cloak of his masculinity fit easily around his shoulders. He was no longer as open and casual as the man she'd once known, but his reserve only added a mysterious, intriguing element to his overall attractiveness.

"I called earlier but got no answer," he said.

"A little after five?" she asked.

He nodded.

"I was in the shower. I quit at five today."

He walked away from her, heading toward the door, but not before she'd seen the way his gaze flicked over her and a sudden blaze leap to life in those gray depths.

"I'll change," he told her. "I picked up some Mexican food at the diner. We'll have it in here." He walked to the door.

"Yes, sire," she mumbled, dipping her head in a bow. When she looked up, it was to meet his black scowl.

"Keep that up, Cara," he warned softly, "and you'll find out just how far I can be goaded."

Not far, she thought when he exited. He was wound

tight, like a spring, ready to uncoil at the slightest jar. She'd better not rile the beast in his den tonight.

She perused the library. With its gun case against one wall and the books lining another, with hunting prints on the wall and large, comfortable chairs, it was a masculine retreat.

It was the room she preferred of all the ones she'd been in. Of course, she'd not seen the master suite yet.

A frisson played over her skin. If Adam made love to her, would he take her to his bed? Her glance went to the tavern sofa, so inviting in front of the hearth. Or there, with a fire dancing in the grate?

Adam's return halted the fantasy, but when she looked at him, she realized the reality was even better. He'd changed to jeans and a red sweatshirt. The denim conformed to his flesh like a caress and snuggled against his hips and thighs, outlining every curve and bulge.

"I'll get the food," he said, his tone harsh.

Cara realized she'd been staring. A flush brought a wave of heat to her face as her gaze met his. With a hardening of his expression, he walked out.

She wondered if she should follow and offer to help, but decided against it. He was the host. Let him play the role.

When he returned with a loaded tray a few minutes later, she cleared the magazines off the coffee table so he could set it down. She saw he'd placed the steaming food on Fiesta platters, one for each of them, hers in blue, his in dark red, which matched their sweatshirts.

"Very appropriate," she complimented his choice.

He nodded absently. After setting the rosewood table in front of her, he put her plate on it and added a glass of cola. "Sorry, I don't have anything more exotic to drink."

"This is fine."

They ate in silence. She noticed the wind had died down and a cloud had covered the moon. It was totally dark outside.

She looked up to find Adam's gaze on her, studying her as if trying to figure out what made her tick. She wished she hadn't taken his job offer.

"I shouldn't have come here," she said.

He left off his regard and gave a snort of unsympathetic laughter. "I agree."

"Why did you ask me?"

He laid his fork down and took a drink before answering. "It seemed like a good idea at the time."

"I think you were lonely."

He flinched slightly at her harsh observation, but he didn't deny it. "Maybe," was all he said. "Why did you accept?"

She shrugged. "Curiosity, I suppose." She wanted to pursue her analysis of him. "Sally said it was hard for you to date anyone in town. The gossips would have you married off before the first good-night kiss."

He chuckled, his expression softening. "True." Giving her an appraising glance, he asked, "What else did you talk about?"

"The town, things in general." She knew she was trespassing, but she continued. "Why haven't you married, Adam? Tradition says you must produce a son to carry on."

His smile changed, becoming at once closed and sardonic. "Are you offering yourself?"

She looked at him without blinking. The tension built as she thought of having his children. Her glance strayed to the sofa where he sat in a relaxed pose, his eyes watchful as she considered her answer.

At last, when the air seemed to shimmer between them, she told him she wasn't. But she couldn't stop herself from thinking of the children they might have had, if things had worked out differently.

He sat forward, his hand striking his knee in a flat slap that broke the silence. "Dammit, stop looking at me like that."

"Like what?" Had her face revealed where her thoughts had flown?

He lunged to his feet and paced in front of the hearth. "You're thinking of what we might have had, the way it could have been between us." At her gasp, he snapped, "Don't you think I've thought of the same thing a dozen times since you arrived?"

"Adam—"

"It was a damn fool thing, writing you that letter. It was done in a moment of weakness." He glared at her, daring her to make something of it.

There was something dark and unfamiliar in his eyes. It almost frightened her. She tingled with unknown stirrings deep within. When she said nothing, he went back to pacing.

"We'll just have to make the best of a bad bargain," he decided, sounding like the executive he was.

Cara almost smiled. He was a man laying out a battle plan, determined to triumph over his libido or emotions or whatever promised to distract him from his goals.

"The important thing is the mill. And the money,"

he reminded them. "If I can get that contract with Beausan in Louisiana..."

"What kind of a contract?"

"To make rain gear out of some new fabric his company has invented. The possibilities are endless— clothing, tents, all sorts of sports stuff. The material is waterproof, yet breathes."

"There's already something like that on the market."

"Yes, but it's a laminated fabric. If it's punctured, it loses its characteristics. The new stuff gets its qualities from the nature of the yarn. If only we had research facilities—"

He broke off, and the light died in his eyes. A flush, as if he'd revealed too much, lightly tinted his neck. He sat back down.

"This is, of course, all speculation. We don't know for sure how the fabric will perform in commercial quantities. I'd appreciate it if you wouldn't mention it to anyone."

"I won't," Cara gave her word.

He trusted her, and she would die before she gave away his secrets or his dreams. With a foreboding sense of disaster, she remembered her own secret goal. Her gaze went to the file drawer containing his personal records. She had to check it, she realized.

"What is it?" Adam asked. "Are you feeling all right?"

For a second she felt threatened by her own nature. She wanted to blurt out the truth and have it all in the open between them. Her confession trembled on her tongue, but she held it back.

Her stepfather had warned her not to tell anyone. The very person she trusted might be guilty. Or know who was guilty. What if Adam knew it was his father, and he was concealing evidence?

A protest rose from deep within her. Adam wouldn't do that. But...what if she was wrong? He was different....

Her head ached with the questions that swirled in her. She would never make it as a professional spy, she admitted. When this was over, when she left Paradise Falls for the last time, she'd never attempt anything like this again.

"Yes, I'm fine," she said, a lie.

"Cara," he said. He sounded strained, on edge.

She looked at him. His hands, with their long, capable fingers that could touch a woman with incredible tenderness, were clasped between his knees, his forearms resting on his thighs.

"It's no good, is it?" he murmured, more to himself than to her. "How did I think it possible for you to come here, to live in my home, and not have this incredible ache for you? I felt the same way when I saw you that summer...an ache that wouldn't give me rest long after you'd gone."

"I know," she whispered, feeling it, too, that wild tang of passion, tart and sweet, as it darted through her.

"How do lives get all tangled and messed up?" He brought his fist down on his knee in a silent blow, then opened his hand and stared at the palm. His glance hardened into anger once more when he raised his gaze to hers. "What the hell does it matter now, after all this time?"

He rose and strode out.

She sighed, letting her breath out slowly. What was that all about? But she knew. She pressed her hands against her chest, which felt too small to hold her heart and lungs and all those yearnings that churned inside. Oh, yes, she knew.

"Good morning." Mrs. Groves smiled and glanced up from the bread she was twisting into a wreath. She laid it on a greased cookie sheet and placed it in the oven.

Cara returned the greeting. "How's your grandson? Adam said he had a fever."

The smile was replaced by a worried frown. "He has. The doctor can't figure out what's causing it."

"You know," Cara mused, "when I was little, my mother said she let me eat some corn off the cob. I only had four front teeth, but she said I seemed to like the corn and was doing okay. The next day I had a temperature of 102."

"Did they think it was the corn that caused it?"

"Well, the doctor wasn't sure, but Mom said as soon as the corn passed out of my system, the fever disappeared within an hour. She's convinced that's what caused the problem."

"Umm, I think I'll tell my daughter about that." Mrs. Groves dusted the flour from her hands and hurried to the telephone.

While she talked, Cara prepared a quick breakfast. She ate the cereal and gazed out the window. Another cloudy day. The sun peeped through the gloom fitfully, as if it couldn't find the strength to make a prolonged showing.

She felt something of the same. Her feelings waffled back and forth between duty and desire. Her duty was to her family, but her desire was all for Adam.

"'O what a tangled web we weave when first we practice to deceive,'" she murmured. "For sure."

In the bright light of day, without his presence to complicate the issue, she was sure she knew what she was doing. The minute he appeared—

"Well, I passed on your experience. Maybe they can find something from that," Mrs. Groves said, hanging up the phone. She cleaned the bread-making debris from the counter and put away the canisters. "I'm going to the hospital as soon as I get done here. There's chicken for sandwiches in there for your lunch." She pointed to the refrigerator. "I'm making a beef stew for dinner. Is there anything else you need?"

"No. Wait. Yes, there is." Cara put her coffee cup down. "Do you recall hearing Mrs. Clairmont mention any records or receipts for the furniture? Some of these pieces are valuable. Surely they kept some kind of file on the antiques."

Mrs. Groves thought about it. "No, I don't remember it, but that's not saying there isn't a list. I've seen boxes of stuff stored in the attic. Oh, have you looked in her desk?"

"In the library? Yes."

"No, no, not the men's desk. Mrs. Clairmont's desk. Where she did all her letter writing."

"No. Where is it?"

"In the master bedroom. A big, glass-fronted desk with pigeon holes and slotted drawers to hold paper and envelopes." Mrs. Groves nodded. "Yes, that's the place to look. Mrs. Clairmont was a stickler on keeping track of things. Check there."

"I suppose I should, before I do any more cataloguing," she decided, standing. She placed her bowl and spoon in the dishwasher. "I hope your grandson is well soon."

"I'm sure he will be. I really think it was something he ate." Mrs. Groves looked hopeful.

Cara took her coffee and went down the hall. The door to the library was open. Adam was nowhere in sight. She assumed he was at the mill, but she didn't know it for a fact. She should have asked the housekeeper.

She approached the master bedroom as if expecting a wild beast to burst out of it at any minute. Mocking her caution, she stiffened her spine, walked up to the closed door and knocked.

The sound echoed along the dim hallway with its eighteen-foot ceilings. No answer.

The hair seemed to creep on her neck. She waited. Footsteps sounded behind her. She whirled around.

"Go on in," the housekeeper called down the hall. "I'll be down to straighten up when I finish the library."

Feeling foolish, Cara turned the brass knob and pushed the door open. She peered around the empty room. Another doorway, through which she could see a shower enclosure, opened to her right. With a mental grimace at her own timidity, she entered and was immediately swamped by the intimacy of the room.

Adam's slacks, the ones he'd worn last night, were tossed across the arm of a blue velvet Queen Anne chair, the pant legs trailing on the Oriental carpet. His shirt lay over the back.

A Chinese bowl of the finest porcelain resided on a pedestal display table next to the entry door. It was filled with coins. His pocket change, she guessed.

The bed was a high four-poster, the kind popular

at the turn of the eighteenth century. The sheets had been pulled up and smoothed, but the blue velvet spread lay folded across the bottom of the mattress.

A question rushed to the surface of her thoughts—had anyone ever shared it with him? She looked away.

The scent of his cologne enticed her to the bathroom door. The shower stall was still beaded with water, she saw. A brush lay on the Italian tiles next to the sink. She imagined Adam there, a towel around his waist, while he shaved.

Reaching out, she touched the damp towel hanging on the rack with fingers that trembled. She'd never taken a shower with a man, but she'd read about it. The couples always made love with the warm water pouring over them, their hands slick and soapy on each other. It sounded erotic and romantic and yet, bonding.

A burning knot of emotion formed in her breast. She closed her eyes, willing it away. Sometimes...sometimes she felt she'd missed all the important parts of living.

Mentally getting herself in order, she pushed away from the bathroom door and headed for the mahogany-satinwood desk, a Hepplewhite "gentleman's secretary" of the 1780s.

Mirrors with gilded scroll edging were set into the upper doors. Behind the doors were books. Cara perused the shelves, finding all the "great" authors— Milton, Browning, Shakespeare—represented there. She could imagine Mrs. Clairmont reclining on the Greek Revival divan to read.

After pulling the drop-leaf down to form the desk, she peered into the eight pigeonholes. Nothing there.

Mrs. Clairmont must have cleaned them out before moving to Florida. The side drawers contained stationery and a roll of stamps. The stamps needed four more cents to make them valid.

The bottom drawer was empty, but the side doors disclosed modern Pendaflex file folders on pull-out racks. Eureka! In a file clearly marked FURNITURE was the information she needed.

Inside the big folder were manila folders, one for each room of the house. Her job would be considerably easier. And faster, she realized.

Sitting on the floor, she checked her list for the two upstairs bedrooms against those in the file. They matched, except for one vase that was missing. It had probably been broken, but she would keep an eye out for it in the other rooms.

She went upstairs with the appropriate information and began checking off the items in a third bedroom. Having the inventory helped, but she had to be sure each item was correctly identified. Several of the pieces were originals.

At one o'clock, she went down for a solitary lunch. A plate had already been prepared and left in the refrigerator. She stripped the plastic wrap off and found a chicken sandwich with tomato wedges, carrot slices and pickles on the side. Mrs. Groves was thoughtful.

After the meal she went into the library.

Pausing in front of the file cabinet, she stared at the bottom drawer for a long time before dropping to her knees in front of it. With a hand that shook slightly, she took hold of the handle and pulled. It wasn't locked.

With equal parts guilt and curiosity, she peered into Adam's "junk" drawer. The files weren't labeled, but she soon discovered the contents—his income tax reports from the past twelve years, his high school and college diplomas, a fraternity membership...and a postcard she'd written him while on a week-long vacation trip with her folks that lovely, lovely summer of their romance.

"'Wish you were here,'" she read the note aloud.

Memories swept into her consciousness. She'd called Adam as soon as she returned, and he'd come for her when he got off work at the mill. She could still recall the drive to the bluff...the plundering kiss...Adam pulling away, breathing heavily. It had grown harder to part from each other with each date.

The shrill ring of the telephone made her jerk guiltily. She hastily dropped the postcard into the folder she was holding and stuffed it back into place in the drawer. She lifted the receiver after closing the drawer. "Hello?"

"Cara? Hello. It's Mom."

"Oh, hi," she said, almost giddy with relief.

"How are things going?"

Cara heard the unspoken question behind the words. "Fine. I found a list of the furniture along with the receipts. Most of the antiques are genuine. Adam has a small fortune in the house."

A silence followed. "Are you alone?" her mother asked.

"I think so," Cara answered. She looked toward the open door and listened intently. Not a sound.

"I suppose you haven't found anything of...real value?"

"Nothing unusual," Cara answered just as cautiously. She felt like Mata Hari on the job. Her scalp tightened. "Mrs. Clairmont has a nice Hepplewhite secretary of the Salem style."

"I see."

Cara heard the undertone of disappointment. They'd had such hopes for this scheme. "But there's the Washington set in the dining room. I haven't checked it or the rooms downstairs yet. Adam said I could look over the office furniture, too. No telling what might turn up."

There, that sounded innocent enough, she thought. In case anyone was listening.

"How long do you think you'll be there?"

"Another week, possibly two more." Cara twined her finger through the spiral telephone cord. Anything could happen in that length of time.

"Be careful," her mother advised, then added, "on those mountain roads. You know how dangerous they can be in the rain."

"I know." She unwound her finger. "How's Thomas? Does he still want me to look for old spinning wheels?"

"He's fine, and yes, he wants any kind of American memorabilia that you can find. Iron pots and kettles are in demand."

"Okay. I'll make some trips through the countryside and keep a lookout for them. Perhaps I'll find some old spinning wheels at the mill."

"Good. Well, that's all for now. Take care."

"I will. Bye."

Cara hung up and sat in thought for a long minute. Finding the person who committed a crime eight years ago had little chance of success and made no difference to her father. If it wasn't for her mother and for the sake of family pride, she would drop the matter, get her job done and get out of town—away from Adam and rekindled desire and the anger and doubts between them, she added. Dear God, life could be so impossible.

Picking up her notes and lists, she returned to the upper bedrooms and worked steadily through the afternoon, not stopping until night had fallen. Realizing she was both tired and hungry, she went downstairs to return the folder to the secretary.

After putting it away, she paused, then opened the mirrored door again and studied the items neatly lined up on the shelves. She skipped the books. Instead, her hand hovered over a leather volume while she wrestled with indecision. Just as she started to withdraw the photo album she'd noted earlier, she heard a door opening in the back of the house.

A second later, footsteps sounded along the hallway. She put the album in its place and closed the door. She'd just opened the file when Adam stepped inside his bedroom door and stopped, his expression instantly wary.

"I found the list," she said, turning to him. "Your mother had the furniture inventory in her desk. Mrs. Groves told me where to look."

The tension grew while he observed her for a long minute, then he nodded. "Good. That should speed things up, shouldn't it?"

"Yes." She crossed the room. "I was just going up to shower before dinner. There's a beef stew."

"I know. Mrs. G. left a note on the refrigerator."

She swept past him, careful not to let any part of her touch any part of him. She'd once had something special with him, but that time was gone, destroyed by circumstances in which they'd been minor players.

She *mustn't* reach back for what could never be. Life had to go forward. There was still her personal goal to finish. She had an obligation to see it through. She would do her best.

But once in the shower, with the warm water running over her like a long-forgotten caress, the tears came…a brief flood, hot and urgent and filled with needs she couldn't suppress.

Chapter Five

"**I** want you to meet my secretary. She'll help you find what you need. She has keys to all the warehouses and offices."

Adam led Cara past his office to that of the secretary. Jenny Boswell was an efficient-looking woman in her forties or fifties, Cara guessed. She was well groomed and had a friendly but brisk air. A basket of needlework sat beside her desk, a basket of fruit on top of it. After the women exchanged greetings, Adam took her upstairs. The second floor evidently wasn't used anymore and was eerily silent.

A few minutes later, Cara was alone in a large storage room stacked with old desks and office furniture. Dust coated every surface like a thin shroud. Although she'd dressed in jeans and a casual shirt, she removed a bib apron from her purse and tied it around her before starting her examination.

While she worked, she couldn't keep her mind from roaming through the minefield of the past week.

Adam had worked late every night at the mill. At the big house he took a plate with him into the library and read reports. Cara had rarely seen him. She'd managed to shove her old feelings for him back into the tattered box of memories where they belonged. What was past was past.

She'd spent Saturday and part of yesterday finishing the house inventory. To her keen disappointment, no clues had leaped out at her from the drawers and shelves of the furniture.

Later she'd had Sunday dinner with Sally and some other old friends. That had been gently nostalgic, like stepping back into the past to a time before her life had so drastically changed.

After returning to the house, she stopped by the library on the way to her room and told Adam she was ready to start at the mill. He'd agreed she should start today. So here she was.

At midmorning, she was on her hands and knees, peering at a small table tucked under a large desk.

"Cara," Mrs. Boswell called.

She jerked in surprise and banged her head on the desk.

The secretary found her by following the sound. "I'm so sorry. I didn't mean to startle you. Are you all right?"

"Yes. It takes more than a bump to put a dent in my hard head. That's what my mother always said."

Mrs. Boswell smiled in relief. "I have something for you." She held a cup in one hand and a paper plate with a Danish pastry in the other. She offered both to Cara.

Cara got to her feet. "Mmm, cinnamon, thanks." She pulled out a chair, took a seat and set the treat on the dusty desk. "It was kind of you to think of me." She smiled at the older woman.

"Adam sent it. He said you didn't eat much breakfast."

Sitting across the kitchen table from him, her appetite had fled. She kept thinking of how things might have been during the brief meal. "Oh. Tell him I said thank you."

"I will." Mrs. Boswell smiled and left.

At noon the lord and master himself appeared. Again she was startled by a voice, but fortunately she was examining a desk from the top side and didn't hit her head.

"How's it going?" Adam asked.

She spun around to face him. He was in his shirt-sleeves, the cuffs rolled back to disclose tanned forearms. He looked elegant, but casual. His expression was remote. She smiled. "Fine."

"I didn't realize this stuff was so dusty," he remarked, not returning her friendliness.

She took his remark to mean she looked as grimy as she felt and brushed self-consciously at her apron.

"Here." He handed her his handkerchief. "Your face."

After wiping her face with the pristine cotton, she handed it back, noting the dust streaks.

"You missed a spot." He stepped forward and wiped her cheek. Then, obviously without thinking about it, he looped the material over his finger, licked it and proceeded to clean her face.

Cara stood very still. It seemed natural, this sharing of intimacy. She knew it was dangerous. She could tell that by the heat that flared in her.

When his gaze met hers, she saw the realization of

his action dawn on him. He glanced at her mouth, then moved back. He stuffed the handkerchief into his pocket.

"Thanks," she said. The mood needed lightening. "For the clean-up and the food earlier. I was famished."

He looked over her, pausing at her old-fashioned apron. "I see you've learned to come prepared."

"Yes."

He glanced around with a frown. "I should have had this place cleaned last week."

"I've seen worse," she assured him. "Do you realize you have a treasure trove here?"

"No."

He didn't seem very interested. Instead he appeared preoccupied with internal thoughts, none of which he wanted to share with her. She gave him a brief rundown on the wooden desks and other items she'd discovered.

"Shall I list them for auction?" she asked. "They're not antiques yet, but a few pieces are collector's items—"

"What's the difference between antiques and this junk?"

"The government defines antiques as items at least a hundred years old. Cars become classics when they're twenty-five, but furniture has to be a hundred."

He gave a wry grin. "The Porsche is a classic then."

"That's right. I can arrange to sell it, too."

He shook his head. "No, thanks."

"For income tax purposes, we'll need to know what you paid for these as well as the heirlooms at your house. Do you know if you still have the records? Most companies keep inventories.''

"The old accounting records are stored in the room next door. Ask Mrs. Boswell for the key.''

Cara calmed the thumping of her heart. It had been almost too easy. Guilt swept over her. She felt she was using him for nefarious purposes. He was wary of her on a personal level, but otherwise he seemed to trust her implicitly. It made her goal seem that much harder.

Clearing her father's name wasn't an underhanded scheme, she reminded herself. Adam's father hadn't felt sympathetic toward her family. He hadn't come to the defense of Stephen Gardner, but had sat silent and withdrawn during the proceedings. She shouldn't feel guilty.

"Good," she told Adam. "I'll make a list first, then look for purchase orders and receipts. If there's none, I'll have to make some assumptions about their original cost.''

"Will the IRS take your word?" he asked, an amused smile lifting the corners of his mouth.

"Yes," she said defensively. "I'm considered an expert.''

"Expert," he repeated, his gaze going to her lips again. A flicker of emotion passed through his silvery eyes, something dark and mysterious and wholly male, something she didn't think she'd seen before in him. Something wholly female in her wanted to answer that flash.

She realized another thing. She was just as attracted to this Adam as she'd been to the younger one. For a second she was tempted to respond in kind; to meet his stare and issue a feminine challenge that no red-blooded male could resist.

She sighed and faced reality. The spell was broken.

"Are you ready for lunch?" he asked. "We have a cafeteria."

"I don't usually eat lunch when I'm working."

"Today you will."

The new Adam, she reflected, was more autocratic than the handsome young man of her youth.

They went to the cafeteria. It was a large room that had been added by Clayton Clairmont soon after he took over from *his* father. He had felt the workers needed a hot meal and a pleasant place to relax at midday. Families were allowed to attend. Cara and her mother had eaten there more than once with her father.

Shortly after she and Adam filled their trays and sat down, Cara became aware of surreptitious glances their way. When she would look up, though, the other diners would glance aside.

"You'll be the object of every wagging tongue in town tonight," Adam said. "Do you mind?"

She shook her head.

"It's a relief to be with a woman and not have to worry that I've compromised her reputation."

"Because I don't live in town," she said, understanding his predicament with the townsfolk because of Sally's remarks.

"I've never brought a woman here," he continued.

She had nothing to say to that. They ate in silence for a while before she thought of something. "Do you miss your law practice?"

"Sometimes."

"Why stay here?"

"How can I walk out?" he demanded philosophically. "To close the mill would mean the end of this place. My ancestors settled here generations ago. One of them started the first mill in the area, and the town grew from that. I'm responsible—" He stopped speaking as if embarrassed by his disclosure.

"Noblesse oblige," she said softly.

"Nothing that grand," he denied. "Just stubborn, I think."

"But if you had your choice, what would you rather be doing?"

"I'd return to the law. I like contract law, browsing around in old legal texts and court records. It's an interesting glimpse into human character."

That made her laugh. "How do you find it among all the *whereas*es and *wherefores*?"

"You have to read between the lines." A smile appeared on his face, and his gaze locked with hers.

Cara felt she was burning inside, lit to incandescence by his amused regard. She wondered if they could have overcome their family problems, if their love could have survived.... It was too late for those thoughts.

With a supreme effort she looked outside. "It's raining," she observed.

He followed her glance to the broad windows of the cafeteria. "Yes, it has been for about an hour. It'll freeze on the roads tonight. Be careful going home."

"Yes, I will." She patted her mouth and laid the napkin on the tray. "I'd better get back to work. Are there any other rooms or warehouses I need to check?"

"No, that's the only one with furniture. The rest hold current inventory."

* * *

Adam walked her back to the corridor where their paths split. He let her go alone up the stairs to the storage area. In his office he began for the third time to review the contract that would sell the mill to a big conglomerate company.

He hated the thought of selling. Things were running along smoothly now, but if the mill ever closed, it would put close to five hundred people out of work. Five hundred families without means of support. Selling to the conglomerate would assure the mill's future, but it would change the character of the town.

So maybe he was trying to be a bloody hero.

Maybe. Or maybe he saw the place through a rosy haze. He'd been born here. His values and sense of right had been formed here. Quite simply, this was his home. He wanted it to retain the qualities he remembered.

If he could work a deal with the Beausan Thread Company on their new yarn and put in the new equipment to make the clothes…that would assure the future of the place. Then maybe he could get back to his life.

He rubbed his eyes against an unfamiliar tightness. He had to stop telling Cara bits and pieces of his dreams. Like today, about law practice, and last week, about his schemes for an international market and the new Beausan yarn. She'd been out of his life for a long time. In a week or two she would be gone again.

He thought of the kiss they'd shared. She'd responded, freely and fiercely, to his caress. He fought the memory, but the fact was, he wanted very much to kiss her again.

* * *

Cara finished her task three days later. Every item in storage was numbered and catalogued. With the advice from several conversations with her stepfather, she had assigned prices. There were two things left to do—search the records for an inventory of the original costs and inspect Clayton's old office and list his furniture.

She tapped a pencil against one palm as she considered what she should do first. The files, she decided. That was the most likely spot to gather some clues. She went to Adam's secretary.

"I'm through listing the furniture. Now I need to check the inventory records. Adam said you had the key to the archives?"

"I had one made up for you." Mrs. Boswell removed the key from her desk and handed it to Cara. "I'll also need a copy of your lists for my files."

"Of course." She hesitated. "Would you check with Adam when he has a moment and let me know if he wants to go over the items, in case some are of sentimental value to him?"

Mrs. Boswell nodded. "I'll tell him as soon as he gets off the phone."

"Thanks." Cara returned upstairs. It wasn't until she inserted the key into the lock and noticed the trembling of her fingers that she realized how tense she'd become.

After entering the dim room, she flipped on the light and closed the door behind her. For a moment she felt claustrophobic as she surveyed the file cabinets, row after row, stacked back to back with just enough space between them to open the drawers. Then she began checking the content labels.

Soon her head was spinning from the amount of information. The records went back, year after year, for over a hundred years—although Cara knew the mill was even older—then they abruptly ended. She decided to start with the most current year and work her way back, checking for inventories.

Taking a seat on the floor, she began going through the prior records. When she came to the year her father had been accused of embezzlement, she slowed her methodical search and became engrossed in the correspondence.

She read through the forms the company had had to fill out, the letters from the accounting firm who had audited the books and a brief note from an attorney asking Clayton to let him know his decision regarding the Gardner case.

She gripped the attorney's letter and closed her eyes against the rage. *The Gardner case.* As if her father was just a number in a file, all in another day's work. As if lives hadn't been changed forever. As if hearts hadn't been broken...

She pondered the information she'd read. She felt so close to the truth. It was waiting for her... somewhere in this room...somewhere close. She was positive there was evidence that would exonerate her father once and for all.

"Find anything?"

Every nerve in Cara's body jolted. She gasped and opened her eyes to focus on Adam standing at the end of the row, watching her with a narrowed gaze. She looked down at the letter and saw she'd crushed it between her hands.

"No," she said. "Not yet." Even her voice shook.

She couldn't still the trembling of her hands as she smoothed the crumpled letter and attempted to replace it in the folder.

Adam came down the aisle and took it from her. He read the brief note before shoving it back into the folder she held. He took the folder, found the place and stuck it back in the drawer.

"I suppose you couldn't resist going through the files for that year," he said. His tone was flat, resigned.

Cara gave him a defiant glare through the tears that shimmered and blurred her vision. She heard him curse vehemently under his breath and slam the file shut. The noise echoed through the room.

The next thing she knew she was being lifted to her knees, her head pillowed against his chest while his arms locked around her in a fierce embrace that shut out the rest of the world.

"Why did I ever ask you to come here?" he demanded in a low growl. "I knew, from the first day you arrived, I knew this place brought back memories. Dammit, Cara, why do you let it hurt you?"

She shook her head helplessly. The tears spilled over onto his shirt.

He stared into her face and cursed once more. Then his mouth came down on hers as if the very intensity of his kiss could blot out the past and all that had gone before.

She wanted to protest, but his tongue invaded before the words could be formed. He kissed her wildly, with the full force of his anger, his dark male hunger unleashed. She was drowning in the flood of his desire, and she was frightened of the man Adam had become, this man she didn't know.

And yet...and yet...when the pressure eased, she wrapped her arms around his neck and sought to ride the tide ever higher.

With a muffled groan, Adam released her mouth and kissed along her neck until he reached her throat. With swift, impatient skill, he unbuttoned her shirt, pulling it from her jeans as he went, until he could push the material to either side of her.

He touched her again, gently this time, sliding his hands around her waist and along her spine up her back. Without words, he guided her, and she let herself glide down until she lay on the oak planks, his body pressed over hers, one leg intimately seeking its place between her thighs.

She felt his lips begin a moist exploration above her breasts, leaving a trail of hunger everywhere he caressed. With his tongue, he traced a line along the edge of her bra and dipped into the shallow declivity in the center of her chest.

He rocked his hips against hers, and she experienced a thrill of yearning as he pressed against her. She moved toward him.

Holding himself on his elbows, he drank her in with his eyes. "Witch. You always made me...wild."

"You make me that way, too," she confessed, rubbing her hands over his shoulders, then spearing her fingers into his hair.

A brightness had sneaked inside her and turned her on. Cara felt she was glowing.

"Wild?" he asked. He dipped his head and licked her bottom lip as if savoring an ice-cream cone. It was so intimate an action that it took her breath right away.

At her soft gasp, he smiled and drew back. He rubbed against her, letting her feel the full impact of his masculine desire for her. A throbbing sensation, like waves of heat, pierced her.

"Your mouth makes me think of blackberries growing wild and sweet along some hidden fencerow. Long after you left, I used to wake from a sound sleep, hot and restless, with the taste of you in my mouth, and knew that I'd been dreaming of you."

Tears filled her eyes. She tried to blink them back before he could see.

"Berries have thorns," he continued, his gaze on her mouth moody and sensual. "I should remember that, shouldn't I?"

"Yes."

"But when I see you, when I ache for the taste of you, I forget." He pushed her hair off her forehead and kissed her there, token kisses that make her impatient for his mouth on hers.

She lifted her face.

"You want more?" he demanded. "So do I. I want you to touch me...you'd probably be shocked at just how I'd like you to touch me. And I want to touch you." He showed her how.

She trembled with the forces he unleashed. She ran her hands over his back and along his hips.

"Yes...*yes*," he said fiercely.

He met her silent demand with a kiss that seemed to steal a little bit of her soul. So much had been lost between them. She arched against him, trying to span a distance that felt like miles rather than inches.

With an eagerness she couldn't disguise, she met the hot thrust of his tongue and explored the coffee-flavored taste of his mouth with the same precision he'd shown toward her.

Seconds rushed into minutes, and still they lay on the dusty floor, wrapped in each other while the world dissolved.

He moved first, his hands finding the fastening of her bra. He freed it with a quick movement. She whimpered when he followed the edge of the band, then suddenly pushed it aside and glided his hand over her, cupping her in his palm.

"You were always so responsive here. I want to see you," he whispered. His voice was ragged, his breathing hard. "Oh, Cara, I have to—"

He eased away and pushed the material up, then he gazed at her, his expression one of fascination. She wanted more from him, much more! He smiled when she shifted restlessly under the heated perusal. "You were shy, the first time you let me look at your breasts, remember?"

She looked into his eyes and was lost, the past and present becoming hopelessly mixed. She nodded.

"You didn't want me to see your beautiful body."

"I know. It was taboo, but I couldn't say no," she confessed. "No one but you had seen me like that. It was...wonderful...and...like wildfire...so very hot...all that sensation."

He closed his eyes.

"Adam?" She was alarmed by the pain she saw in him.

"You were so incredibly sweet," he murmured. "It made me ache when I held you. I couldn't sleep after I left you...I wanted you so. I think I would have sold my soul...."

"Yes," she said, remembering. "Me, too."

He rested his forehead against hers for a second, then he began kissing her all over her face, covering it inch by inch. "I'd never been the first love of any-one but you," he said. "I've never forgotten the way

you were when we met...untouched and yet so willing...melting in my arms. My first love."

"I didn't know how to kiss." His lips burned a
trail over hers. "You showed me." She gasped as his
tongue touched hers with liquid fire. "With my mouth
open. It was so...it made me feel..."

"Wild," he said, placing little love bites at the corner of her mouth. "So innocent. And yet...there was
all that promise locked within you. And you were
willing to let me in. I could have taken you...that
summer...all your sweet innocence..."

"Adam, we shouldn't be remembering. It's no
good—"

"It's too damned good." He breathed against her
lips. "It was the sweetest gift anyone had ever offered
to me. Offer it again."

He covered her, taking his weight on his arms but
surrounding her with the solid strength of his body.

"So hot," she moaned softly. "You make me
feel..."

"How do I make you feel?" he demanded with a
low groan of pleasure when she twisted against him.

"As if I hurt, but I don't know where. You make
me ache." Tears seeped from the corners of her eyes,
and she crumpled his shirt with her eager, restless
hands.

He paused, then laughed, a low snarl of threat and
plea-sure. "I make you ache? You baby, you don't
have any idea..."

When he surged against her, his own aching need
made plain, she trembled wildly. Deep in some secret
place, flames erupted, but here in his arms she had
no thoughts of danger, only a sense of a yearning
about to be fulfilled. She caressed him urgently.

The courthouse clock chimed the hour. "We have to stop," he said, drawing back from her. "I can't take you here. Not here. Not now."

His meaning only dimly penetrated. She wanted to continue, and she didn't care about the floor being hard and dusty. She didn't care that there wasn't soft music and firelight.

"Umm," she protested when he pulled her arms from around him and sat up. She raised herself and laid her head against him, hearing the harsh pounding of his heart in her ear.

"I have a meeting. I have to go." He took hold of her arms with fingers that hurt and roughly propelled her to her feet as he rose to his. He straightened her clothes and fastened her shirt.

Cara stared at him, still shaken by that untamed rush of passion. Suddenly she was horrified. He could have taken her right there. She'd wanted him to. She licked her lips, unsure what to say.

He laid a finger over her mouth. "Don't say anything. You can't deny what happened anymore than I can, so don't try."

"I'm not denying it." She pushed the hair from her forehead and realized she must look tousled and very much kissed.

He studied her for a long minute. "Let the past go," he advised suddenly, harshly. "Let it be decently buried with our fathers. This delving—" he indicated the drawer she'd been searching "—it only hurts you."

"It wasn't your father who was accused of wrongdoing."

With a stifled exclamation, Adam turned and walked away, creating a cold draft around her. "Be sure and lock the door before you leave,'' he said. He left.

She leaned on the file cabinet for support until her legs felt strong enough to take her weight again. Adam knew she was digging through the files. He'd suggested she stop, but he hadn't actually forbidden it.

Was he pretending to be concerned for her, or was he afraid she'd find something against his father? Had he— She put a hand over her mouth to stifle a cry. Had he deliberately distracted her with passion?

She shook her head in denial. He wouldn't. She knew he wouldn't. That had been honest passion.

Whatever happened between them, she couldn't leave now. She was close to discovering something. She could feel it, a premonition so strong it was like being taken by a strong wind and whirled toward some destiny that only the fates knew. She had to ride it out.

Chapter Six

On Friday night Cara ate quickly, then checked the paper to be sure of the time for the Historical Society meeting. Her investigation was about to take a new direction. She was going to start asking questions and interviewing people. The sound of a car interrupted her planning.

In a moment Adam walked into the kitchen. "Hello. Anything left to eat?"

She'd hardly seen him since that episode in the file room. He looked grim and tired. His secretary had mentioned the negotiations with the Japanese conglomerate. Perhaps they weren't going well. Mrs. Boswell said Adam wanted some guarantees the other company wasn't willing to give.

"There's a pot pie and cheese bread." She checked and found the food still hot. "Have a seat. I'll get you a plate."

She ignored the glance he gave her before taking her advice and sitting at the table. She gave him a

plate and silverware before pouring a cup of choco-
late-flavored coffee for him. After reheating the crusty
slices flavored with cheese, she served him before re-
suming her place at the table and sipping her coffee.

He broke off a piece of bread and dug in after
giving her a perfunctory thanks.

She contemplated the slow fall of evening while he
ate, and tried not to let his presence bother her, but
she kept remembering his hands on her, touching her
with passion...with reverence, too. As if she were
precious.

Tears burned behind her eyes. She swallowed hard
as emotion churned in her chest. At last she looked
at the clock on the stove. "I have to leave now."

"How about dessert?" He looked up with a frown.

"I think Mrs. G. said there was a chocolate cake."
She stood. "I'll cut a piece for you."

"I can do it," he cut off her offer and gave her a
chilling smile. "Big date tonight?"

"I've made plans to attend the Historical Society
meeting," she said, ignoring the sarcasm in his voice.

He studied her as if searching for a motive for her
behavior. "It'll bore you to death. Miss Josie and old
man Wagner take turns reading their latest research
findings."

"Actually, some professor is going to talk about
preserving family records. It sounds interesting." And
she sounded stubborn, she realized.

"I'll drive you," he volunteered, putting down his
cup.

"You're going?" She couldn't hide her astonishment.

"Why not? I'm a member in good standing."

"What about dessert?" She frantically tried to think of something imperative to keep him at home.

"I'll have it when I get back." He stood. "Let's go."

During the ride Adam didn't speak at all. She finally asked if he wanted to go over the list of furniture, for keepsakes. He said no and asked if she were about through with the job.

"Actually I've catalogued everything but your father's office and the attic at the big house."

"It won't take long for the office. There're only a few things left in there. All the files were moved to my office."

She hid her disappointment. "Well then, I'll just finish checking the inventory files. Mrs. Boswell is helping when she has time. We found bills of lading for some of the office furniture."

"She told me."

Cara refrained from demanding to know if he'd sent the woman to spy on her so she couldn't look through the records. One more week. That was all the time she could take without making it obvious she was dragging her feet. Perhaps tonight at the meeting she would come up with something.

"I made three lists—one for the good stuff, which I can handle," she told Adam. "One for the items you can probably sell to a second-hand store. And one for things you can junk. Selling the office furniture will free up your storage space in case you need it. There's an old wooden loom that would look nice on display in the entrance hall at the mill, a piece of history for visitors to examine."

"Sounds good," he approved, but she could tell his mind wasn't on the discussion.

Cara was acutely conscious of him on the brief ride, of the spicy scent of his after-shave and the way his hands confidently guided the car along the winding streets of the town.

When they pulled in front of the Historical Society building and stopped, she noticed the name over the door. "The Frank G. Wagner Historical Museum," she read aloud. "Why did they name it after him?"

"Probably because he donated the building and the money to remodel it to the society."

"Oh, yes, Sally mentioned that."

A drumroll of excitement pulsed through her veins. Mr. Wagner, the chief accountant under her father, was moving to the forefront as the prime suspect. He would have had the opportunity to doctor the books; now it looked as if he had a motive. A bachelor with no children to carry on his name, he had insured his immortality through the museum. The fact that he'd bought the old hotel seemed significant, too.

She could hardly wait to get inside and start asking questions. But she had to be subtle about it. After all, she couldn't just march up to Mr. Wagner and demand to know where he had gotten the money for a hotel and this building.

"Adam, it's lovely to see you again," an elderly lady in flowered silk exclaimed when Cara and Adam went inside. She checked his name in a book. "You haven't been to a meeting in almost a year."

Cara recognized Josephine Smith—Miss Josie to three generations of English students at Paradise Falls High.

Adam ignored the reprimand. "I brought a guest.

She was interested in coming. Do you remember Cara Gardner?''

"Of course I do. She was an excellent student." This was apparently the highest recommendation the woman could give.

"Miss Josie remembers everything that ever happened in town," Adam said with a wry grin.

Cara couldn't tell if he was teasing or warning her. Had the woman known about her and Adam? Was that why she'd mentioned her work in Beckley to him? Cara signed her name hurriedly in the guest book while the spinster looked on with interest.

"Are you visiting in town?" Miss Josie asked. "You used to be friends with Sally Winetski, didn't you?"

"Yes, but I'm doing some work for Adam," Cara said.

"You appraised my sister's furniture in Beckley. Antiques." She snorted. "Junk, if you ask me, inherited from her mother-in-law, who told everyone she was connected to the Lees of Virginia."

"Some of the pieces were very good," Cara murmured. She didn't add that most of them had been reproductions.

Adam made small talk with the retired teacher, but Cara didn't listen. She looked around, wondering if Mr. Wagner was there yet. She had to talk to him. Alone. The meeting was called to order.

She waited impatiently until the speaker for the evening finished his talk on preserving old family Bibles and such for future historical reference. Adam sat beside her, his arm occasionally resting on the back of her chair. When the social hour began, she stood and scanned the room.

"Who are you looking for?"

Cara faced Adam. He was too astute. She decided to confuse him by being honest. "Mr. Wagner. Is that him over there?"

He followed the direction of her gaze. "Yes."

"Would you excuse me?" she asked. "I remember him from before. I'd like to say hello." She scooted off before Adam could voice the questions she saw forming.

She was relieved when he didn't follow her, but stopped instead to talk to someone else. She was equally glad Sally hadn't attended; otherwise, she'd not have had a moment on her own to pursue her line of investigation. She approached Mr. Wagner. Would he recognize her name?

"Mr. Wagner, I'm Cara Gardner," she announced herself. "My family used to live in Paradise Falls."

The old man—he must be in his late seventies—squinted his watery blue eyes and studied her. "Stephen's girl?" he asked.

"Yes." She observed him intently. No jerk of the hands, no gasp for breath betrayed guilt as he held out his hand.

"You were just a little thing last I saw of you," he said.

"Eighteen. I was eighteen."

He nodded. "I heard about your father's heart attack. I'm sorry. He was a good man. I always thought so."

He sounded so sincere and looked so innocent. She felt the pressure of tears behind her eyes. Questions crowded and locked in her throat. *Did you do it? Were you the one who made the changes in the books to implicate him?* She said nothing, only nodded her head.

Mr. Wagner asked, "What are you doing now? And your mother, how is she?" His interest seemed genuine, not morbid.

"Fine. She's married again, to a wonderful man. They live in Roanoke. I work for Townsend Auction." She spoke in brief sentences while memories from the past intruded. Mr. Wagner had always been kind to her. Was that a cover?

"Have you noticed the changes in the town?" he asked, beaming with pride.

"Yes. I understand you bought the hotel after it was renovated." She paused. "And donated this building to the society. That was generous of you."

"Well," he said with a modest manner, "I wanted to do something for the town. People have been good to me here. I was a stranger, you know." His face clouded for a second, then he smiled again.

Cara wondered if he was remembering his fiancée who had died so tragically. Her heart went out to him, and she couldn't think of a single probing question to ask.

They spoke for a few minutes on the changes in the town over the past few years, then she excused herself. She talked to several others, including the mayor and chief of police. She pretended an interest in people she'd once known, all of whom had worked with her father, and asked questions on their whereabouts and welfare. At the end of the evening, she knew little more than when she started. Dismally she realized she wasn't getting anywhere. She needed a more decisive plan.

She saw Miss Josie coming toward her, curiosity

bristling like spines on a cactus. "Tell me about your antique business," the woman demanded in good-natured tones.

Good-natured, but still a busybody, Cara thought while answering several more questions.

"Did your father like being in business for himself?"

"Yes, I think he did. At least, he didn't say he didn't." Cara began to feel a little desperate. Miss Josie could certainly ask probing questions. Like many older people, she seemed to think age gave her the right to be inquisitive.

"Hmm," Miss Josie said when Cara finished her recitation on her family. "Do you have a boyfriend back in Virginia?"

"Uh, no." Cara looked around the room for Adam. When their eyes met, he seemed to get her message. He came to her at once.

"Tomorrow's a workday," he said, taking her hand. "Are you ready to go?"

Miss Josie, evidently not pleased with Cara's evasive answers concerning her life, stared pointedly at their linked hands. Before she could comment or ask about their relationship, Adam said good-night and herded Cara out the door.

In the few minutes it took to drive up the hill, she composed herself, thankful for the dark night and for his silence.

At the house she headed for her room. Adam caught her arm, holding her captive. She looked at his hand, lean and dark against her white sweater. "Adam—"

He nodded toward the kitchen. "We were going to have dessert when we returned."

"You were. I'm going up to bed."

"I'd like to talk to you."

"What about?" she asked, alarmed by the harsh gleam in his eyes. He looked like a prosecuting attorney ready to pounce and wring a confession by force if necessary. He was an attorney, she reminded herself. He could probably think of probing questions without any effort at all.

"You." He gave a tug on her arm.

With definite sensations of uneasiness, she followed. Her thoughts leaped ahead. Adam was probably going to warn her off her investigation. He had to realize that's what she was doing. Perhaps she could talk him into helping... No, he was the enemy.

Except he didn't feel like an enemy anymore. He was Adam, the man she'd once loved. It would be easy to fall in love with him again. *Don't,* she warned herself.

She wanted to turn toward him, to rush into his arms and let him comfort her. She longed to be held by him, close to his warmth. To experience his kisses, the way his lips roamed her face, tantalizing her mouth. To know nothing but the searing heat of fulfillment in his arms. She wanted all those things. No, no, no.

At the kitchen he released her. "Sit. I'll put on the coffee."

He worked efficiently, getting the coffee ready, the cake cut and served. When he joined her at the table, they ate silently.

"Do you want a glass of milk?" he asked.

She shook her head. When they finished, he put their dishes away and picked up his mug. "Let's go into the library."

She followed him and sat in her favorite chair. The moon, she saw, was a slightly larger icicle tonight. She shivered.

Adam knelt at the hearth and built a fire, again with an ease that bespoke skill. When he had the flames jumping over the logs, he sat on the arm of the sofa, his thigh close to hers.

"Your hair shimmers in the firelight as if it's filled with embers. I want to warm my hands in it."

She stared at him, startled by this development. She'd been expecting a confrontation, not this.

He suited actions to words by sliding his hand into the thick waves and grasping a handful. He lifted it and sniffed. "I like your fragrance."

His eyes were so dark and broodingly deep she thought she could lose herself in them. Unable to stop, she raised a hand and stroked the lock of hair off his forehead, then let her hand rest on the side of his face for a second.

For a poignant moment they stared at each other.

"Are you going to tell me what you're doing?"

Disarmed by his tenderness, confused by the low harshness of his question, she could only gasp, "What…what do you mean?"

He let go of her hair. "I mean all those innocent questions you asked tonight. Whatever happened to so-and-so," he mimicked her bright chatter of the evening.

She clenched her hands together, then held them still. "I was just curious." She laughed. "Nosy, I guess."

"Miss Josie is nosy. You're after something. What?"

"Nothing."

He gave an exasperated snort. "Don't give me that. Do you think I can't put two and two together? You asked about every family and individual who worked with your father. What are you up to, Cara?"

"Leave me alone, Adam."

He drew a deep breath and let it out slowly. "I can't. You won't let the past alone, so I can't leave you alone. I have to know what the hell you're doing."

She refused to speak.

"Let me put it another way—do you want to talk about your father?" He pinned her with the force of his stare.

Life seemed focused on that one moment, as if everything that would happen to her from then on was dependent on the outcome of this one instant in time.

"What about him?" Her voice quavered, not much, but enough for anyone with a suspicious mind to detect. Adam was trained to discern fine nuances.

"That's what I'm asking. What are you looking for?"

"Proof," she said, giving in to the forces inside her that prompted her to be open with him. She lifted her head and gazed up at him. "Proof that he didn't take that money. That someone else did."

"So it comes back to that." He rubbed his fingers across his forehead. "The past is never dead, is it? It casts its pall on all the days that follow and fools that we are... Well, it doesn't matter now."

She regretted her burst of honesty. She could take a lot from Adam, but ridicule for her loyalty wasn't on the list.

"It does matter." She got to her feet, her hands clenched at her sides. "My father thought Clayton

Clairmont was his best friend, but your father prosecuted him.''

"He had no choice. The insurance company, the state attorney, the accounting firm, all were pressing for charges. The case couldn't be dropped. Fifty thousand dollars had disappeared."

"My father didn't take it."

He stepped in front of her. "Then why can't you drop it? Your father was cleared—"

"But he never recovered from the humiliation. There were always suspicions because the real culprit was never found. Until that happens, there'll always be a cloud over my father's name. Those people at the meeting tonight, I saw the questions in their eyes as they wondered 'Did he or didn't he?' I mean to find out."

The crackling of the fire filled the silence.

Then, "How?" Adam asked.

She sighed and turned from him. "I don't know. I'm not making any progress. I thought…maybe the records at the mill would disclose…something."

"But they haven't?"

She shook her head.

Adam was silent, thinking. "You think my father might have done it and shifted the blame. Why?"

She shrugged. "Gambling debts, maybe. Blackmail for some scandal. I don't know."

"My father put in a hundred thousand dollars of his own money to keep the mill going. He had to weigh the life of one man against the lives of five hundred families who would suffer if the mill closed." He had become cold and remote again, the lord of the manor speaking.

"Then it was someone else. My father never stole

anything in his life," she said. "He was innocent. I'll prove it."

The silence stretched like nerves too tightly leashed for too long. "Have you found anything at all?" Adam asked.

"No. But there must be a clue somewhere, some little slip the criminal made that will prove his guilt. I'll find it." She rubbed her eyes, then absently noted the mascara on her fingers.

Adam sat on the stool next to the hearth. He stared into the fire. "I'll help you," he said.

Cara shook her head slowly. "Why?"

"I'm sworn to uphold the law. It's my duty to find the truth." He studied her for a minute. "If we find the truth," he asked coldly, "will your need for revenge be satisfied?"

"I want justice, not revenge. Revenge requires hate to fuel it," she told him. "I've never hated you, Adam. Never." She went to her room without waiting for a reply.

Adam was waiting for her the next morning. He invited her into the library after she ate breakfast. He picked up a legal pad from the desk and read down a list.

"It would be the purest chance if you happened upon something in the mill files. Those records go back for generations, until the fire in 1880 burned down the place. My great-grandfather had to rebuild from scratch."

She'd assumed someone had thrown them out.

Adam, all business although he was dressed casually in black cords and a gray sweater, continued.

"What we need are the grand jury transcripts and the accounting records."

"Oh. Can anybody get them?"

"Court records are open to all citizens unless a judge rules there's some reason to keep them secret. I'll handle it."

"I...thank you, Adam."

He waved her gratitude aside. "It's in my best interest to get this settled. I don't want anything to jeopardize the merger."

"You really have sold the mill?" She couldn't believe it.

He nodded. "If they accept my proposal not to move or close it for ninety-nine years. In legalese, that's considered forever."

"Then you'll be free to go back to your law practice."

He didn't act overjoyed, only tired of it all. "Yes," he said. "Free. At last." He tossed the pad back on the desk. "There are worse things, aren't there?"

Cara didn't understand his mood. The lives of the Clairmonts had been so bound to the mill that she couldn't imagine either existing without the other. After listening to his plans for expanding the business, she thought maybe Adam felt the same, only he couldn't admit it. Defeat was hard to take.

"We can't start until Monday," he said. "What are your plans for the day?"

"I thought I'd go through the trunks in the attic. I've listed a few pieces of furniture up there. It isn't worth anything. But steamer trunks are in demand. I could sell those and probably any clothing in them, if you'd like."

"Fine." He pulled out a report. "I'll be working in here."

She nodded and left. At the door she glanced back to find him gazing out the window, his expression as hard and bitter as a cherry pit, then he began reading.

Cara went to the attic and looked through the trunks of clothes. Definitely a vintage collection of Victorian costumes, most in excellent condition, but none of museum quality.

In the tray of one trunk, she found a small box, its velvet worn around the edges. Inside she found a pair of opera glasses. She gasped. She'd seen the papers on those and had assumed the glasses were lost.

"Adam!" she called, grabbing up the box and racing down the stairs. "Adam, I found something."

She burst into the study and nearly collided with him. He caught her by the arms. "What is it?"

"Look!" She waved the box in his face. "Opera glasses. Made for Marie Antoinette."

"Should that mean something to me?" he asked, a frown settling between his eyes.

"They're worth quite a bit. A pair sold a couple of years ago for sixty-five thousand at auction. These should do as well. We have the documentation for them. Your mother did a super job of compiling the inventory."

"Let me see." He took the case from her and opened it. The opera glasses—gilded, gem-studded, enameled with scenes of the pastoral life and a miniature portrait of the queen—gleamed against the black velvet of the interior.

"Sixty-five thousand?" he questioned.

"Yes. Will that...will that help you?"

He laughed with delight. "As they say, every little bit helps." He sobered. "This could make a *big* difference."

"I'm glad."

He scrutinized her expression. His smile changed, becoming sardonic, challenging. "Why?"

"I've never wished you, or any member of your family, harm, Adam," she said quietly. He didn't seem to believe she could sincerely be happy for him.

"Well then, everything's fine, isn't it?" He took the velvet case from her. "I'll put these in the safe."

She felt like crying. She wanted him back, she realized, the old Adam who had cherished their love, who had believed in their future, who had thought they had a chance in spite of all that had happened. *Oh, Adam, my sweet, innocent love.*

Blindly she went to her room.

"Hi. Come on in. Everyone's here." Sally held the door open for Cara to enter the Winetski home. Sally's mother had insisted she come over for Sunday dinner.

"Mmm, something smells heavenly," Cara commented, sniffing the fragrant spices wafting from the kitchen.

"You remember Linda." Sally introduced her older sister, who was very pregnant. "She was the one who always bossed us around."

"Would you mind if I don't get up?" Linda asked with a grin. "I think this watermelon might burst if I jostle it too much." She laid a hand on her full abdomen.

"Please, sit still," Cara responded in mock alarm. The women laughed in easy camaraderie. Sally completed the introductions to Linda's husband and their three children. When Mrs. Winetski came out of the kitchen, she wrapped Cara in a snuggly hug against her bosom as if Cara were a long-lost daughter.

Cara found it easy to slip into the old ways with Sally's family. After the meal, she and Sally took the two older boys for a walk over to the woods where, as young girls, they'd played pirate and jungle games so long ago.

The boys immediately started looking for arrowheads along the bluff when Sally told them she'd once found one there.

"So," Sally said, turning to Cara, "the big news in town is that Adam took you on a date."

"It's news to me, too."

"Come on, the Historical Society? That's a big date in Paradise Falls."

"Oh, that date." Cara managed a laugh.

They watched the boys pile up a cairn of stones.

"You've never forgotten Adam, have you?" Sally at last asked.

"I...no, I've not forgotten."

Sally sighed. "Your eyes are sad. Do you still love him?"

For a second Cara's throat closed, and she didn't think she could answer. "There's still something there."

"So what are you going to do about it?" Sally demanded in lighter tones. "Are you going to let him get away? He's still the most eligible bachelor in town."

"Is he? Even if the mill goes under?"

"Adam would be the most desirable male around

even if all he had was the shirt on his back. Ask any female in town.''

"I'll take a poll," Cara declared. She changed the subject. "So when are you going to hook up with someone tall, dark and handsome?"

"When someone like that comes to Paradise Falls," Sally stated. "I'll throw my arms around him and not let go. If he proves too difficult, I'll get Mom and Linda after him until he gives in and marries me."

Laughing, they called the boys and started the walk back to the house. Cara looked at the alert faces of the children as they showed their treasures, some shiny rocks, to their Aunt Sally. One of the boys had dark hair and gray eyes.

Cara suddenly had a vision of the children she and Adam should have had. She could see them, laughing and running in the sun. She wondered if there was a chance to reawaken old dreams. Adam was attracted to her, so maybe there was.

Adam paused at the top of the hill, his breath coming hard. He'd jogged for a solid hour. Maybe that would stop the riot in his blood whenever he thought of Cara.

It was getting harder to resist her. Every day she lived in the house caused another rip in the fabric of his good intentions, which were to leave her strictly alone. His life was complicated enough without the man-woman thing confusing the issue.

He turned and went into the house, aware of its size and the echoing silence in the empty entrance hall. In his youth, he'd thought it a wonderful place, full of adventurous nooks to hide in. His parents had been happy then. The latter years had changed.

He thought of Cara. If they'd married, she would be here, waiting for him. There might even be children to make the old place into a happy home again.

A gut-wrenching ache tore at him. At the same time, passion flared, making him want to bury himself in her, to forget all the things that had happened and live for the moment.

Except he couldn't. Because Cara wouldn't let the past go.

She'd held onto it and let go of their love instead. Eight years ago, the scandal hadn't made any difference in his feeling toward her. He didn't give a damn, then or now, whether her father had taken the money or not, but it mattered to her.

He scowled fiercely. He would try his damnedest to find out the truth, then it would be finished between them. Maybe she'd be able to get on with her life. And he'd do whatever he had to do, with the mill and with his life.

He stopped at the library door. One delicate foot dangled off the end of the sofa. Against his will, he was drawn into the room.

Cara was sleeping, her head cradled on her arms.

Unable to stop the hot burst of desire from shooting through him like a meteor, he took in every perfect line of her—the shape of her face, the slenderness of her waist, the sweet curve of her hips and thighs.

He dropped to the floor beside her and lifted a strand of hair to his lips. It smelled of shampoo and her cologne. He released the curl and brushed the sweat off his face with his sleeve.

Anger spiraled in him. At her for tempting him. At

himself for needing her. Bending, he let his lips lightly touch hers. Just a taste, that was all, just a tiny taste and he'd leave.

It wasn't enough.

He kissed her again, with a little more passion this time.

She stirred, and her lips parted. He probed the opening and found her tongue. It stroked his in a gentle answer to his touch.

Hunger exploded in him. He took her mouth, hard and fast and relentlessly, the kiss scorching him with its intensity. When he drew back, he was breathing as if he'd just climbed the hill again.

Her eyes opened, startled and sexy and alluring as a Jezebel. "Adam," she said, putting a hand up to ward him off.

Her action set off his temper. "Damn you," he muttered. "Damn you for tempting me."

Worry darkened her eyes. "I haven't—" She stopped and clamped her teeth in her bottom lip.

"Haven't you?" He laughed. "Then maybe I was just imagining the invitation in your eyes. Why don't we find out?"

He crowded her against the back of the sofa as he sat beside her, his hand finding the curve of her hip as if it belonged there. He reached for her, need a boiling caldron in him, drowning out his common sense. He ignored the alarm that had joined the passion in her smoky-blue eyes.

She made a sound of protest when he lifted her to him. He could feel the swift rise and fall of her chest against him, torturing him with images of her, naked and flushed, under him, taking him in…

"Adam," she pleaded softly, "don't. I can't think...when you do that."

"You were always this way, wild and sweet, in my arms. Do you remember?" he asked, wanting her to remember, to ache for him as he did for her.

"Yes."

He could have made love to her years ago. He'd been the one who'd called a halt. But now she was a woman, and she was ready. He could feel it in the trembling of her body, in the clinging strength of her arms. He could take her without qualms....

"You never resisted me," he murmured. "You never told me no."

"I couldn't." It was true, she realized. Adam could have made love to her whenever he wanted. He could now.

"I sometimes wonder if it would have made a difference. Would we be together now if we'd been lovers then?"

She shook her head while tears filled her eyes.

"No," he agreed. "Too much stood between us. You didn't love me—"

"I did."

"Not enough." He looked down at the close fit of their bodies. "We could have had...paradise, but you turned away."

He got up and walked out, leaving her alone, desperate for what they'd lost and wondering what other choice she'd had.

Chapter Seven

Cara's emotional equilibrium was restored when she entered the storage room at the textile mill on Monday morning. It was a relief not to feel guilty at digging through the files for her own clandestine purposes and to know she wasn't taking advantage of Adam's trust. That had bothered her more than she had realized.

The secretary walked briskly toward the midsection of the large room. "Here're the accounting records for the past hundred years or so." She pointed them out. "Good luck."

Cara smiled. "If the former secretaries were half as efficient as you, I'll have no trouble."

"Well, I believe they were men until about 1920."

"Oh, dear."

They smiled, then the secretary left Cara alone. She went at once to the year her father had been arrested. After she found the auditor's report, she studied it carefully, particularly the parts dealing with the shortage. The alteration of the records seemed rather clumsy to her.

Her father would never have done anything so sloppy, she concluded. If he'd wanted to steal money and not be caught, he would surely have devised a better plan. After all, that had been his career—managing money for optimal profit.

Footsteps sounded behind her. She turned and saw Adam. "Find anything?" he asked, coming to her. She handed him the report.

He was too handsome to be allowed out on the street; women would forget to watch for traffic as they stared at him, she mused.

There were other things she noticed. The tension which had eased briefly over the weekend was back. While talking to the secretary in her office earlier, she'd heard him speak in the controlled tones that indicated anger while he talked on the phone to someone.

He finished the auditor's report. As if lost in another world, he looked her over, his gaze following every curve of her cherry-colored suit. He tapped the report against one hand. His fingers were lean and restless. She was reminded of his caresses that had made her blood sing.

When he spoke, it was about business. "I've arranged to pick up copies of the transcripts late this afternoon, also back issues of the newspapers. I'll bring them to the house."

"Good."

"It will be a lot to read through. This was the biggest case in the county in thirty years."

"I know."

He eyed the boxes of files that lined the room to

the ceiling. "Junk," he said and, shaking his head, returned to his office.

Shortly before five he stuck his head in the door. "Any luck in here?"

Cara, her apron protecting her clothes from dust, was engrossed in a file folder. She looked up distractedly. "Uh, no. I was just looking at the modernization that's been done in the past few years. I'm impressed."

"It still isn't enough."

"You independents should form a cooperative."

"Have you ever tried to get a flock of chickens to cross a road together?"

"That difficult?"

"Worse." Adam removed the file box from her lap and pulled Cara to her feet. Turning her around, he untied the apron and lifted the bib over her head. Cara's neck burned where he'd touched her. She rubbed the spot.

"Here," he said, his voice deepening.

She took the apron from him and made a job of folding it and sticking it in her purse. She reminded herself of the resolve she'd made during her sleepless night. For eight years, she'd dreamed of clearing her father. That had to come first. She owed it to her family.

"Well, I'm off to the courthouse," he said, "then I'll stop by the newspaper office. A friend promised to dig out back copies on the trial. I'll see you at the house."

"I'll wait dinner," she said, realizing she was hungry. She had worked right through lunch. She wondered if Adam had, too, since he hadn't come for her.

He gave her an odd glance, nodded and left.

The whistle blew at five and the workers left the mill. She waited until the rush cleared, then drove to the big house. There, she showered and changed to fresh slacks and a red sweatshirt, then went to the kitchen to see what she could contribute to dinner.

She made a pot of hot tea, which seemed like a good choice for the meal and for the weather, which was surly. Mrs. Groves had prepared chicken and rice in a wine sauce. Broccoli and carrots steamed on top of the stove.

As evening deepened, the temperature dropped and the roads became icy. She worried until she heard Adam's sports car purr to a stop in front of the house. She dashed to the door and held it open while he brought in a tied package and shoved it into her arms. He ran back to the car for the box of information.

"The weather is really turning nasty," he remarked, brushing sleet out of his hair when he returned. "What happened to spring?"

He looked tired and grumpy, she noted. A wave of tender sympathy swept over her. She wanted to hold him and smooth the fatigue and the day's irritations away. "I think Mother Nature forgot it this year," she said. "Dinner is ready. Shall we take our plates into the library?"

"Yeah." He hurried down the hall. She followed. He put the box on the desk and took the package from her after shrugging out of his trench coat. "I'll build a fire. The furnace won't handle this cold."

"All right. I'll get our meal. I made hot tea. That okay?"

"Sure."

"Anything wrong?"

"No."

Rebuffed by his shortness, she went to the kitchen and fixed a tray with heaping plates of food. She added the teapot and two cups, cheerful plaid napkins and the flatware.

When she returned, Adam took the tray from her and placed it on the coffee table. "It's going to be a long evening," he remarked, glancing out the window at the sleeting rain.

Cara thought his comment sounded cryptic, but when she glanced at him, he was smiling pleasantly enough.

"If you're too tired, I can read through the transcripts alone," she volunteered.

"We both need to go over them carefully to see if we can pick up on a clue. One person might miss something that will leap out at another."

She remained silent for a while. After they were halfway through the meal, she cleared her throat to indicate she had an announcement of importance. When she had his attention, she said, "I've done a lot of thinking since last night. I just want you to know that, whatever we find out, or *don't* find out, I'll accept it. The past will be finished, and I'll pursue it no more."

Whatever he thought of her declaration was concealed behind the immovable mask he wore. "Fair enough."

Lifting her fork, she eyed the box of transcripts and package of newspaper clippings while she finished eating. She wanted to rip into them right away, find the truth and be done with it. She forced herself to eat and wait for Adam.

After their dinner, he cleared the table and made coffee before returning to the library. While he wasn't exactly what she would call domesticated, he was at ease in the house, confident in his masculinity. He gave her the news to read while he started on the transcripts. They worked in silence.

"Listen to this," she said at one point. "The auditing firm said they had an anonymous tip about the moving of funds from the local bank to one in Beckley. Who do you suppose called them?"

"Was Wagner the chief accountant then?"

"Yes."

"Why don't we make plans to ask him about it, if we don't find anything in the transcripts? I'll make a note of it. We should have a list of things we need to check, anyway."

"Right."

Adam glanced at Cara. There was a frown of concentration on her face as she absorbed every word. His glance slid down to the ripe protrusion of her breasts against the red material of the fleecy shirt. He knew she wore nothing under it. His body hardened with a fierce spasm of need. He looked away.

They read until the hour grew late and his control grew lax, his thoughts straying more toward her than the dry court records he was reading.

"Enough," she declared, laying a newspaper aside and rubbing her eyes. "The print is blurring into petroglyphics."

He finished the page he was skimming and got up to add more logs to the fireplace. Aware of their isolation, Adam fought a reckless desire to do something dangerous. To ward off the thought, he asked, "How about some hot chocolate?"

"I'd love some." She smiled up at him. "There's

fresh pecan sandies in the cookie jar, too. Your house-keeper is a jewel.''

"Yeah, she is." He had Mrs. Groves, he reminded himself. But a housekeeper wasn't the same as a wife, a woman who would love him more than anyone else. "Sit still. I'll get it."

Alone in the kitchen he cursed himself for wanting her, but he couldn't stop the urgent flow of heat that gathered in his lower body and danced in his blood.

Hell, he should go ahead and make love to her. That was the only thing that would ease the ache. But would it be enough?

Cara stretched her arms and legs and back, then lay supine on the sofa. The newspaper accounts of the trial didn't bother her the way she had thought they might. Having Adam with her helped. Sometimes that part of her life seemed so long ago, it was almost as if it had happened to someone else.

What if none of that had happened? What if her family still lived here? What if she'd met Adam only recently? Would he have fallen in love with her now?

Tears formed. She rubbed them away, wondering what was taking him so long. She should have refused the midnight snack and gone on to her room. Laying her arm over her eyes, she listened to the whispering sound of the wind and rain against the house. The fire leaped in the grate, its warmth gentle on her...like a caress.

Like Adam's hands.

Adam set the mugs on the coffee table and stood looking at Cara, asleep on the broad sofa. As it had the previous night, her innocence called to him. He wanted to awaken her to passion with him. He wanted her to know how it could be between them. The sweet giving and urgent taking. The selfish demands as passion reached its peak. The sense of oneness...

She opened her eyes, and he saw she'd been aware of him the whole time. Cursing under his breath, he spun from her and the pleasure he would find in her arms.

Cara gave a muted cry and sat up. In his eyes...that raw tenderness... As if she were the sun, capable of giving life and hope and all the desires of his heart. Then it was gone.

"Adam," she whispered desperately, "I never meant to hurt you. *Please...*"

He faced her, his mouth twisted into a mockery of a smile. "Hurt me? You couldn't. A man would have to care to be hurt, wouldn't he?" He gestured to the tray. "Eat up. We still have a lot of work ahead of us tomorrow."

With shaking hands she accepted the cup he gave her.

They were silent. She watched the firelight play over the strong, handsome lines of his face. "Why haven't you been seeing anyone here in town?" The question sprang from her lips in an unguarded response to the pensive expression in his eyes.

He gave her a sardonic grin. "It's been so long since I dated, I've forgotten why we do it."

"I don't believe that."

"Well, you may be right." He wiped a hand over his face as if to make sure no emotion showed. "After the way I've reacted to you, it would be a lie to pretend I don't know why men and women are attracted to each other, wouldn't it?" His laughter was harsh.

"Did I do this to you?"

"Do what?"

He wouldn't give an inch, she thought. He was harder than the rocky crags of the mountain. "Make you hard and bitter toward women."

"You taught me a lesson about love and how it works," he replied.

The tense communication that flowed between them without words was beyond her experience. She sensed the hurt that pride wouldn't let him reveal. She knew he was lonely and weighed down with problems. He also wanted her. It burned like a fever in the twin depths of his rain-washed eyes. She'd never been wanted like that.

"It's late, Cara. Go to bed."

She was still.

With a rough curse, he rose and came toward her. With a hand on her shoulder, he pushed her into a reclining position. Kicking off his shoes, he joined her. For a long moment, they lay there, faces close, not speaking, not touching.

This is how it should be, she thought. A man and woman coming together in the naturalness of time and circumstance, with no past and no future, but only the moment to bind them. She wished they'd made love last night.

He lifted a hand to her face and caressed her. Tears came to her eyes.

"No," he said harshly. "No tears."

"You're so gentle," she explained.

"How else would I be with you? You remind me of summer meadows and wild grasses blowing in the wind and sunny days of laughter. Winter disappears when you walk in the door."

His words were unexpected, a gift. "That's unbearably beautiful." She could hardly speak.

"You're unbearably beautiful."

They spoke in the softest breaths of sound, and he kissed her face a thousand times, kisses that tantalized her with their fleeting touches.

"Kiss me," she finally demanded, her hands brushing restlessly over his chest.

His mouth stopped roaming and settled lightly on hers. He rose up on his elbow and bent over her, increasing the contact between their lips, but still not touching her body.

He turned his head slightly and the kiss became more intimate. When his tongue touched her, she opened her mouth, inviting him within. Instead, he sucked at her lower lip, then the upper one, tasting each as if it were some rare exotic fruit he had just discovered.

She made her own explorations. Swiftly she unfastened his shirt so she could touch his flesh. He was warm, so warm. His chest hair curled around her fingers, holding her to him, and she felt his nipple contract when she brushed over it.

His arms encircled her, turning her on her back, and his body moved partially on hers. When his knee nudged her legs, she moved them so he could slip his leg between hers. Sensation shot off in every direction within her.

Sliding her arms around him, she stroked his back down to the waistband of his jeans, then returned to bury her fingers in his thick, crisp hair. A slight coolness on her side warned her just before she felt his hand glide under her sweatshirt and touch her bare skin. Then he moved upward and cupped her breast. She breathed in sharply.

Ripples of delight resounded through her, echoing

in the beat of her heart, pounding in her ears. Oh, the magic of him, the wonderful, wonderful magic. "Adam," she murmured, urgent and demanding. "Make love to me."

He raised his head and regarded her through half-closed eyes. "I think that's what we're doing."

"Are we?" She gazed at him, entranced by the passion-dark depths of his perusal. "It seems there should be more. I need more. I need—" she stopped as tears suddenly welled in her eyes "—so much," she finished helplessly.

She felt his chest heave against hers. "Take off your top," he said, hoarse and low. He moved so she could sit up, then he raised the sweatshirt over her head and tossed it to the floor. "Sweat heavens," he gasped.

With an exquisitely controlled movement, he bent to her as she lay down. He sought her breast with his mouth. When he closed his lips over her nipple, she moaned and twisted with pleasure.

When her breast was swollen and the nipple engorged, he pushed his shirt aside and covered her with his bare chest, skin touching skin. "You're like satin," he whispered. "Hot, hot satin."

"I've never forgotten the way you touched me," she said, radiant inside. "Your hands...so gentle... always so gentle..."

"I didn't want to scare you. You were young."

He slid his leg against hers, and she felt the lean, hard strength of his body and the tension as he held himself back, forcing himself to go easy with her. His tenderness reached right down to the ache inside her, adding to the leaping flames.

She held her breath when his hand skimmed along

her side, coming to rest at her jeans snap. With a quick twist, he loosened it. With another quick glide, the zipper was open. The lacy edge of her bikini briefs showed between the open vee of the denim.

"Red," he murmured, his voice becoming deeper, huskier, rasping along her sensitive nerves. "My favorite color."

With one finger, he stretched the elastic lace and watched it snap back against her skin. The flames leaped so high in her, she thought she would explode. "Adam. Please." She would beg. It didn't matter. He must come to her....

He kissed her, his tongue delving into the richness of hers, the taste of chocolate mingling in their mouths. Then he explored the groove of her neck, her shoulder, under her arm and along her side until he moistly traced a path to her breast again, nibbling first one, then the other.

"Cara, how careful must I be with you?" he asked.

"I'm not sure." Her voice was tremulous with the passion he'd aroused. At the moment she didn't think he need be careful at all. She wanted him to complete it, to make her whole and stop the yearning that gripped her.

He frowned, puzzled. "Don't you know?"

"Since I've never made love, I don't know what to tell you," she tried to explain. "I don't know what to expect...."

He looked so astounded, she thought she had said something wrong. "You've never...this is...I don't believe it."

At that moment she realized he had been asking something entirely different. Her inexperience had caused her to interpret his question quite differently.

"Oh, you were asking if I was protected, weren't you?"

"Are you?" he asked, no expression on his face.

"Well, no. I had assumed you would…"

"Okay, I get the picture."

He tore himself from her and stood. While he buttoned his shirt, she pulled on her sweatshirt and fastened her jeans. She wished they hadn't stopped. There was an insistent ache inside that she instinctively knew only he could soothe.

"Forgetting your goal?" he asked, waving at the box of court records still to be read.

Cara shook her head. She sat up, pulled her feet under her and contemplated his closed expression. "Don't be angry, Adam. You wanted to make love, too. Why did you stop?"

"Why? I don't deflower curious virgins."

"I'm past that stage. If I'd wanted to experiment, I would have long ago. There's more than curiosity between us." She met his gaze bravely. "Isn't there?"

He pushed the hair off his forehead. "You were right that first time we kissed," he said bluntly, ignoring her question. "Too many complications stand in the way of an involvement between us. There's no future in it."

"Couldn't we start again from now?" She wanted to, with all her heart. She needed him in ways she'd never thought to need another person. If only she'd been more confident in their love and less caught up in family pride and hurt… But she'd been too young to realize what she was giving up.

He laughed, a cruel sound that mocked her question. "And pretend the past never happened?"

"No," she said, sighing and smoothing her hair off her face. "We can't go back."

"We can't go forward, either," he told her. "Not until the past is resolved, like you said, one way or the other."

"I know," she said, gazing into the fire.

"Don't look so sad," he mocked. "Like they say, it'll all come out in the wash."

"I *feel* sad. I hurt you, and I'm sorry. I'm so very sorry."

The silence in the room rang with recriminations and bitter regrets, with hopes that vanished into thin air. His rejection beat like a death knell in her heart.

"You'd better go up," he finally said.

She rose and walked past him to the door. "Thank you for getting the transcripts, Adam. I...it's my problem. I can go over them by myself."

He shrugged. "I said I'd help, and I will. We'll take the day off from the mill and start at nine in the morning."

Adam woke sluggishly, the rumpled covers testimony to his restless night. He glanced at the clock—eight—he had an hour before he and Cara were to start work. The sky outside his window was dark with clouds as the storm system lingered over the central part of the southeastern United States.

Usually quick to rise, he lay in the bed and contemplated his life. Since Cara had reentered it, nothing had been the same.

He hadn't realized how empty the days could be until he compared them to being with her. He hadn't allowed himself to think about it, but the past two weeks had been...good.

Too damn good. The worst mistake he could make was to get that crazy over a woman again. He'd learned his lesson the first time. There was no need to repeat it.

But he couldn't help remembering she was a virgin...like she'd been at eighteen, inexperienced yet eager for him, letting him take her as far into ecstasy as he wanted...giving him that sweet, wild passion he'd found only with her.

Fires ignited him. He balled a fist and struck the bed, helpless to fight the erotic sweep of passion.

A virgin. Because she'd not found anyone since she'd known him? Because what they'd shared had been so deep, so complete, so overpowering that nothing else even came close?

He swore, softly and eloquently.

Forget it. He had enough things on his mind. He had devoted years to solving the company's—and the town's—financial future. The talks with the conglomerate were moving along. All he needed was a reopening of the old embezzlement case to throw a monkey wrench into the works.

In addition, the house was a liability. It took a monstrous tax bite each year, and he doubted he could sell it anytime soon. Until he disposed of the mill and the old mansion, he was tied to the town by a tradition that went back almost two hundred years.

Damn, but he was tired. No wonder his father had looked gaunt and troubled the last few years of his life. He had died at his desk at the mill, working alone one Friday night. A massive brain hemorrhage from a tumor.

Everything had seemed impossible until Cara came. Now he found himself entertaining hopes that the conglomerate would agree to his last changes in the contract, that he could sell the mansion and thus have some cash to start a new law practice, that somehow he and Cara could— He cursed his too-active imagination.

He closed his eyes, but all he saw was her, there in his bed, held fast in his arms, letting him love her....

He flung the covers back and headed for the shower. "A cold one," he muttered, slamming the door behind him.

The phone rang while he was getting dressed. He answered and listened while the head of the textile division of the conglomerate told him his plans to come to Paradise Falls.

"Here?" Adam repeated when the man finished. "Today?"

Just what he needed. Damn.

"The board thought some of us should meet with the local people, test the political climate and all that before we finalize the contract. I'll be bringing in a new manager to learn the ropes. He wants to check out the town and school system."

"How many and when will you arrive?" he asked, resigning himself to the inevitable.

"Two—myself and Ted Hardt. We'll fly into Beckley late this afternoon and rent a car. Hardt wants to see what kind of road you have up there. We plan on spending the night and looking the town over. Do you have time to give us another tour of the plant?"

Double damn.

"Sure. I'll look forward to it." He invited them to

stay at the big house. May as well take advantage of the place. One thing, it was impressive. The executive accepted. They exchanged a few more pleasantries and hung up.

"Triple damn," he muttered in disgust.

He dressed in casual clothes and headed for the kitchen. He needed coffee, strong and black. Cara was already there, enjoying the breakfast Mrs. Groves coaxed her into eating every morning. He nodded to her.

"We have a glitch," he announced.

Both women cast him a questioning glance.

"I have guests arriving later today to look us over. The head of the textile division of the conglomerate wants a tour of the town. I've asked him and the new manager to spend the night." He spoke to Mrs. Groves. "This is short notice, but can we put on a spread? Maybe one of your dinners will impress the heck out of them and make them forget the town is in the boondocks and there's only one road into the valley, and it's torture to drive."

Cara picked up her cup and hid behind it. She didn't want to acknowledge the bleak humor in his words. Adam had his pride, too. To sell the family business, even if running it wasn't his first choice for a career, must hurt.

"Of course." The housekeeper poured him a cup of coffee and handed it to him. "Sit," she urged. "I have blueberry pancakes."

Her eyes met Cara's briefly. In their blue depths, Cara saw a plea for her to do something. She looked away. What could she do to help Adam? Exactly nothing.

Grabbing a dish towel and using it as a pot holder,

Mrs. Groves removed a warm plate from the oven and set it in front of him. "I'll go through my best recipes," she assured him.

"If you're having guests, perhaps I should see about moving to the inn," Cara suggested. He gave her such a hard look that she fumbled for an explanation. "I don't want to be in the way."

"How would you be in the way? With an entire floor of guest rooms, I hardly think we'll have to ask anyone to double up."

His irony was hard to take. She wanted to sympathize, but he wasn't having any. A spurt of anger warmed her blood.

Mrs. Groves spoke up. "You'll be needed. Mrs. Clairmont always said a woman was necessary to keep the men civilized, especially in difficult situations. She used to play the piano after dinner."

"To soothe the savage beasts," Adam added, his mouth tilting into a sardonic smile. "Mrs. G. is right. I thought you might help entertain. Unless it would be too much trouble for you."

It was a challenge she couldn't resist. "No," she said, just as cool as he.

The realization that she would, in effect, be his hostess set her pulses to thrumming. It was worse than foolish to pretend, but she couldn't help it. One tiny dream out of a lifetime—to be with him as his partner for one evening. It couldn't possibly do any harm to live the fantasy once. Just this once.

After eating, they retired to the library to resume their task. Adam called the office to alert his secretary to the visit of the buyers and dictated several memos to his managers. Then he took a stack of transcripts and set to work. Cara felt she was imposing on his limited time.

"We need to see if we come up with some suspects," he told her. "Someone with a grudge against your father or someone—"

"I already have two," she broke in. "Mr. Wagner is the first. He had the opportunity, and I found a possible motive at the Historical Society meeting. In fact, you mentioned it."

She wondered how he could kiss her and be so hot for her, then be so cool when next she saw him. He seemed able to negate the wild passion that bloomed between them at the slightest contact and to focus instead on solving the case.

Regret flashed through her, raw and punishing. Shame followed in its wake. She'd offered herself to him. She'd asked to start over. He'd refused.

Now if she could just get over wanting his arms around her every minute.

"What motive?" he prompted when she was silent.

"Well, he's a bachelor, with no children. What better way to achieve immortality than by having a museum named after you? You said he endowed the society with the building.... Why not?" she demanded when Adam began shaking his head.

"Mr. Wagner's sister married Lawrence Asher, who not only owned the old Asher mansion, but about half the town, too. When the Ashers died without heirs, old Wagner got everything. He now owns the hotel, the shopping plaza—"

"Okay, he's independently wealthy," she said. That only left Adam's father. She saw his lips draw in tight against his teeth as he realized where her thoughts were.

Adam's face changed, almost looking soft for a minute. "It's hard, isn't it?"

"What?"

"Life."

She nodded. "More than I thought it could be, and it has seemed terrible at times in the past."

Adam gave her an assessing study. "You're not cut out to be a detective."

Determination crimped the corners of her mouth. "I have to." She sighed. "But I feel guilty."

"Guilty?"

"Like at the mill," she explained. "I felt so guilty. I thought you could surely see why I was so anxious to poke around in the archives."

"To gather evidence," he concluded.

"To *find* evidence. When I went to the Historical Society meeting, I felt as if I were using people for my own purposes." She paused, frowning. "The worst thing is, I *am.*"

"Why don't you forget it?" he demanded suddenly. "You're wasting your life on something that's over. Your father was cleared—"

"No, he wasn't," she argued, keeping her voice low, but unable to prevent the fierceness from coming through. "He was released for lack of evidence—it was impossible to tell who'd altered the bills and records—but he wasn't found innocent. Until he is..."

She stopped, realizing she was becoming emotional. Unlike Adam, she couldn't maintain a facade of unfeeling stone.

But when he spoke, there was an undertone of strong emotion in his voice. "Until he is, you're committed to searching for the proverbial needle, or clue in this case, in the haystack."

"I made a promise, to myself and my mother, and no matter what, I have to try to keep it. How can I do less?"

She cast an imploring glance at Adam. He stared back, as implacable as a pagan god. She shivered, realizing she wanted the comfort of his arms, and that he would never allow it. He'd given her a chance to come to him years ago. There wouldn't be another.

"I wish I had never come back here," she said, despair eating at the twin wounds of familial pride and long-lost love.

"But you did, and now we'll see it through to the end." He looked as grim as she felt.

Chapter Eight

Cara swallowed the pain in her chest and got on with her task. She worked all morning on the transcripts. Adam was interrupted several times by calls. Once he had to go down to the office to straighten out a problem with a supplier. She realized how truly demanding the mill was on him.

On all the calls she overheard, he never lost his temper once. Twice he patiently explained to the shipping foreman why he wanted an order unpacked and checked again before shipment.

"We've fouled up two orders for these people. Once more and we'll lose their business. I want you to check the invoice and make certain we're sending what they wanted. That's your job, and I consider it the most important in the business. Our customers have to be satisfied. I'm depending on you."

When he hung up, he caught her watching him. She couldn't prevent the admiration from coming through.

"You handled that very diplomatically. I don't think I would have been so kind."

He shrugged aside her praise. Her opinion obviously wasn't important, and she was embarrassed for speaking out.

"Kindness gets things done faster than anger." His smile was grim. "I've tried it both ways."

She went back to reading. When she next stood up, it was to find him watching her, speculation in his gaze. "Yes?"

"How long do you think you'll be here?" he asked.

Raw grief assailed her. He wanted her gone. "I'm finished. No, I have your father's office furniture to check," she corrected, "then I can leave." *With my conscience intact,* she added silently.

And she would leave having done a good job for him and Townsend Antiques—which had been her first task—and her best for her father's memory. She realized she'd been foolish to think she could do more.

"We have another day's work here." He indicated the stacks of information. "You can finish up at the office on Friday."

"I can finish tomorrow."

"You'll be busy tomorrow."

"I'll take the transcripts home with me. My mother can help me dig through the rest."

"I wasn't referring to those." He indicated the stacks of records. "You agreed to help me with the buyers."

She was astounded. "All day?"

"Why not? A foursome is better than a three-some." He paced the room like a caged lion, a mane of dark hair falling over his forehead, which was creased into a frown as he thought. "We'll take them to the Asher Inn for lunch. Call Sally and see if she can join us. She can give a glowing report on the town's growth potential or something like that."

"All right." Cara realized she'd fallen in with his plans without further ado.

"They have to be at the airport at seven for the flight back to New York, so we don't have to worry about dinner tomorrow. We'll give them a snack at four."

"Teatime."

"What?"

"That's teatime. What about bringing them back here to relax over some of Mrs. G.'s scones and jam?" She laughed. "Watercress and cream cheese sandwiches...we should do the whole bit. The house is the perfect setting for it."

Adam nodded his approval. "We'll use the conservatory. Order lots of flowers for it. And wherever else you think we need them."

"Right." She scribbled notes to herself while they talked. "Should we take them over the ridge to the rumored resort area? That might impress them. We could point out the fun residents have on the lake and river."

"Good idea. No, wait. That road is murder."

"Tell them you've heard there's supposed to be a new road to connect the town with the interstate highway soon. That would be the truth. I've heard it at least three times since I've been here. We don't have to go into detail." She wrote some more.

When he didn't respond, she peered over her notes

to see what he was doing. He was studying her with a knife-edged gaze.

She'd probably done it again—jumped in where only fools and angels dared go. "Yes?" she asked when he continued to stare.

"Do you always respond so freely with your help?"

"When I care about something." She looked back at the paper, unwilling for him to see her foolish heart in her eyes.

"Will this delay upset your schedule?"

She shook her head.

"Then we'll finish up the court records on Thursday, and you can finish at the office on Friday."

"And leave Friday afternoon," she concluded. "I should be done by noon."

His mouth, which had been relaxed, tightened as if she'd made him angry again. This mature Adam had become much harder to predict, she thought.

"Do you have to rush back to Virginia for anything?"

Why was he asking? "No, but..." She clasped her hands together to hide their tremor and waited.

"There's a dance at the inn on Friday night. I thought you might like to go. You've done nothing but work since you arrived. Some of your old classmates will be there. A couple of them asked if I'd bring you."

A dance. First he'd asked her to be his hostess, now to go to a dance. She felt her heart plunge on a rock slide of emotion.

"Well?" he demanded.

"That sounds like fun."

"Good." Satisfied, he picked up the phone and dialed his secretary on the intercom. While they talked, she went to talk to the housekeeper about the work to be done. Later he called it quits and told her to take a break.

"Have lunch and rest," he advised. "I have to go to the office for a while."

The house seemed lonely when he left.

"Lobster bisque to start, then mixed green salad, beef Wellington and apple tarts with sharp cheddar melting over them. How does that sound?"

"Wonderful, Mrs. Groves." Cara looked over her list. "I think we've accounted for everything. Now let's keep our fingers crossed that it all works out."

"It will," Mrs. Groves predicted. She was amazingly calm.

"Do I need to do anything special around the house?"

Mrs. Groves had called in a friend, and they had given the house an extra-special cleaning and prepared the guest rooms for the two men Adam would bring home with him that evening. Cara was nervous about her role in entertaining the men.

"Well, Mrs. Clairmont liked to do the flowers herself. She had them on the dining table, in the hall, oh, and the library. She used to serve coffee in the library after the meal. I suppose Adam will want to do the same."

"Umm, yes, I think so." Cara tapped the pencil against the table. "Sally said a classmate of ours had bought out the florist. I'll call her shop and ask her to deliver the arrangements. I don't do flowers. Oh, we need them for the conservatory. Adam said to order lots of them for the tea party."

"Tea party. What will we be doing next—Shakespeare in the parlor?" Mrs. Groves grinned and went back to the stove, where something savory for dinner was cooking.

Cara went over her lists. Three men and one woman. Perhaps Sally could come to dinner, too. Going to the library, she called.

"Sorry," Sally said. "I have a closing at six tonight. It's one of the hazards of being a Realtor. Your time is not your own. Do you want me to scout up someone else?"

"No, that's okay. I'd be nervous with anyone but you."

Sally laughed. "Thanks for the compliment. I think. You make me sound like an old shoe, comfortable and dependable."

"You are," Cara told her. "Can you meet us for lunch tomorrow? Give them a sales pitch on the town."

"Yes. I'll polish up my chamber of commerce speech. I have to go. My client just drove up. Take care."

Cara echoed the farewell and hung up. She was on her own tonight. She glanced at her watch. It was time for her to start her bath. Adam was still at the office. He had worked sixteen hours a day all week, part of it helping her. She wanted to make this evening perfect for him.

Returning to the library, she finished the records she'd been working on, but without the hope that had sustained her when she'd arrived in town. She knew she wasn't going to find anything in them she didn't already know or suspect.

After storing the records and straightening the library, Cara went upstairs and showered, then studied her clothes. She'd learned to travel with outfits that could be adapted for several occasions. The forest-green skirt that reached her ankles with the white silk blouse embroidered with green silk vines on the wide collar? Yes. The single strand of pearls and matching earrings her mother and stepfather had given her last Christmas would provide the finishing touch.

She considered her hair. Should she let it cascade in waves around her shoulders as she usually did? Something more was called for, she decided. She dried it, then tied it at the crown and coaxed fat curls to dangle along her neck.

After putting on her makeup, she dressed in the outfit, slipped on black pumps and went downstairs. The flowers had arrived. The three formal arrangements were on the hall table. She put them in place. The rest had been scattered around the glass-enclosed room on the south side of the mansion.

In the kitchen, Mrs. Groves put the finishing touches on the apple tarts. She slipped them into the oven. "Don't you look pretty," she exclaimed, approving Cara's choices.

"Thank you. Those tarts are going to make the house smell wonderful, like a holiday."

"Umm-hmm. The weather seems right for them."

Cara glanced out the window. After a few paltry days of sunshine, the sky had turned dark and threatening again. The wind rushed at the house from all sides, and tree branches raked the bricks like banshees scrabbling to come in.

"A good night to be inside. I hope it clears by tomorrow, else the tour might not be a success," she worried aloud.

"The weatherman says it will," Mrs. Groves assured her. "Well, everything is ready. I'll serve appetizers in the library. The fire is laid. Just strike a match to it."

Cara took a deep breath and went along the hall. She started the fire and stood in front of it, just staring mindlessly into the flames until she heard the men arrive. She turned to greet them.

The sight of Cara standing in front of the hearth, the flames casting a rosy aura all around her, took Adam's breath when he escorted the guests into the room. From the expansive smiles on the faces of Miller and Hardt, the scene affected them the same way.

She was...*beautiful* seemed inadequate. Her outfit was that of a fairy princess, the green vibrant against the dark red-brown of the fireplace bricks. The fire picked out the auburn lights in her hair and cast a rosy shade on her white blouse until she seemed to glow with her own inner radiance.

She was *woman*—a gentle, delicate being; ethereal, haunting, and yet so real and honest and human. No wonder men lost their heads over them. And their hearts to them.

He wouldn't do that again, he vowed, swallowing against an obstruction in his throat. It was becoming harder to hold on to that resolve, he realized.

"Cara, this is James Miller, head of the textile division of STI. Ted Hardt will be the on-site manager in Paradise Falls. Cara is...an old friend."

She flicked him a quick glance. He saw the sympathy in the depths of her eyes, which seemed to deepen to a darker shade of smoky blue. He didn't need her bleeding heart act.

"Good evening," she said in her silky-smooth voice, a slightly husky quality underlying the words.

"Good evening." The manager, a slender man with white-blond hair, whom Adam judged to be about his own age, rushed forward and took Cara's hand after Miller greeted her. "The end of the journey makes the trip worthwhile," he declaimed like a minor poet of the previous century. His eyes ate her up.

Heat surged through Adam's body. It forged his hand into a fist that wanted to smash Hardt's unctuous face. He went to the bar and asked for cocktail preferences while pouring Cara a glass of white wine. The men told him what they wanted.

Cara took the glass from Adam with a murmured "Thank you." She gave him a sharp, warning glance. His manner was overbearing. Giving her the glass of wine without asking was an act of intimacy. It made it clear to the other two men that he knew her tastes so well he didn't have to inquire, and that she would accept his choice for her. Possessiveness wasn't like Adam.

"I'm glad you arrived before dark," she said. "The view of the mountains from the road is lovely, isn't it?"

Adam frowned at her for mentioning the twisting road. She smiled serenely.

"The most spectacular place is the Vista Point at the bluff. It was my favorite spot as a teenager. Also all my friends." She grinned wryly at Ted Hardt, inviting him to laugh at the juvenile dating practice of "parking."

Hardt and Miller responded on cue. Their laughter flowed over and past her, leaving her with a faint chill. Cold men, she thought, instinctively not liking them.

Adam handed the men their drinks. He cast her a hard glance. She noticed that he had taken a glass of wine for himself.

They sat and talked of the weather until Mrs. Groves appeared at the door, gave a slight nod to her and disappeared.

Cara stood. The men immediately got to their feet. She linked a hand over the arms of their guests. "Gentlemen, shall we dine?"

The meal slipped by as pleasantly as warm butter dripping off the homemade rolls Mrs. Groves had prepared. Each course was perfectly cooked, perfectly served. The two women exchanged pleased glances when Cara indicated it was time to retire to the library after the sumptuous dessert.

Mrs. Groves had replenished the fire, she noted, marveling at the woman's forethought. The coffee service was ready, too.

"You should give that woman a raise," she murmured to Adam when she handed him his coffee cup...without asking his preference in cream and sugar as she'd done for the other two.

Adam glanced heavenward as if asking for relief from women's demands, then he smiled, a singularly grateful smile that thanked her for her help. For that second, looking into each other's eyes, they were in accord and all felt right with the world.

"Do you...ah...live in town?" Ted Hardt asked, settling on the sofa beside Cara. He was obviously fishing for information on her situation with Adam. As if she'd be interested in a man like him after knowing Adam. All during the meal, their attitude of being the men-with-the-money had come through.

"Actually I live in Roanoke." She sighed. "Like you, I'm here in a working capacity. Adam asked me to update the records of the antiques in the house. Most of the furniture is quite valuable, such as that Tiffany lamp with the butterfly motif and the other with the trumpet flower design…quite valuable," she repeated to be sure they understood Adam had assets they might not be aware of. "And the dining-room suite belonged to George and Martha Washington. Priceless. I know a score of people who'd kill to own it…if I could convince him to sell."

Having made her point, she changed the conversation. "Where are you located now?"

"Near Boston. We have to close that plant or rebuild before the end of the year. It's been condemned—"

The harrumphing of Miller stopped the confession of problems at their other textile site. She glanced at Adam. He gave her a very discreet grin. The conglomerate needed the mill more than they wanted known. Adam could drive a harder bargain for the town.

They talked until midnight, then Cara stood and suggested it was time for bed. The men went upstairs to their assigned rooms. She lingered in the library while Adam banked the fire.

When he turned to face her, his expression was pensive. "You were a great help tonight," he told her.

"I'm glad."

The silence spun between them.

She pressed a hand between her breasts. Her heart

seemed to have moved there and was thudding against her breastbone.

"You'd better go up."

She nodded.

Another ten seconds passed. His gaze strayed over her, outlining the curves of her body. She trembled.

He took a deep breath and let it out audibly. "I'll walk you up," he said. He took her hand, intending to lead her from the room and the temptation of the long plush sofa. In her eyes was understanding...and a longing that matched his own.

But when he touched her, they didn't move.

"Lie down," he murmured. "I want to hold you."

She did without hesitation, kicking off her evening shoes without a protest and stretching out on the tavern sofa.

He threw off his shoes and suit jacket and joined her. He laid his hand on the curve of her hip. He was at once aware of layers of cool silk and warm flesh under his hand. He wanted her—that would never stop—but more than that, he needed to hold her.

After sliding one arm under her head, he let himself roll against her so that they touched everywhere. She opened her thighs and his slipped naturally into place between them. He sighed and closed his eyes.

The air shimmered around them, warm and rosy with the glow of the dying fire. A flame leaped across a log with a hissing sound. An ember brightened, winked and faded.

Outside, the wind had died with the passing of the storm. All was quiet. They slept.

Cara woke to the subtle sounds of someone moving in the room. She was still locked in Adam's arms. His eyes were closed, his face relaxed in slumber. Adam's jacket covered them.

Raising her head, she saw the housekeeper lighting fresh logs in the fireplace. Rising, Mrs. Groves saw her watching and smiled. She placed a finger over her lips and silently went out.

Cara lay there snug in Adam's arms while the room warmed and the sun came up over the mountain. She was the happiest she'd been in years. For an hour she spun daydreams, then Adam stirred.

He looked at her in confusion, then his eyes cleared. He gazed at the fire. "You didn't do that," he said in a sleep-husky voice that sent a shaft of hot desire right to the core of her.

"Mrs. Groves was in earlier."

"I suppose we should get up. It's almost seven." But they didn't stir.

He pushed his face against her neck, and she felt the moist sensation of his lips and tongue tasting her. During the night he'd held her to him without caresses. Now he began to stroke her body. Soon she couldn't resist moving against him, needing more.

He sighed, his breath a tiny hot tempest on her skin. "A first," he whispered. "I've never woken with a woman in my arms."

Her heart danced crazily at this confession. She wasn't foolish enough to think he was as inexperienced as she was, but she was glad he'd never shared this with anyone else.

She arched against him.

"Are you always like a cat in the morning?" he asked, a teasing light joining the dark passionate flames in his eyes.

"I'm stretching." She covered a yawn and glanced

at the clock. "We have to get up, or else be embarrassed if we're caught slipping into our rooms at this time of the day still in our clothes from last night."

"Maybe you'll be embarrassed, but I won't," he told her with the frank assurance of the arrogant male.

She punched him in the ribs.

"But you're probably right," he conceded. He placed a quick kiss on her lips and swung up and off her. He held out his hand.

This time they made it out the door. At the steps she paused. "I can find my room from here." A flush rose in her face at his comprehending perusal.

"I want to brand you mine," he told her with a sudden intensity that surprised her. "I see the way Hardt looks at you, and I want to tell him to back off or I'll do it for him."

"Adam!" she exclaimed softly with a glance up the stairs.

He gave a savage curse. "Remember that today, when he makes a pass at you."

"They're the buyers," she reminded him, shaken by the fierce jealousy he didn't bother to hide.

"I don't give a damn who they are. If he touches you, tell me. He won't do it again."

She laid a hand on his cheek. He turned his face and kissed her palm. "Don't jeopardize this chance," she warned.

He looked into her eyes. "I don't intend to."

She went upstairs and slipped into her room. While changing from her dress to fresh clothes, she mused on his last statement. She thought…she was pretty sure that they had a chance after all.

"A happy, well-knit community makes for good employees, I've found," Sally said, speaking from her experience.

Cara kept a straight face. She had during the entire two-hour lunch, while Sally had deftly answered every question about the town and its happy denizens. She met Adam's glance. He winked at her while keeping his expression pleasantly solemn.

When the luncheon concluded, she and Sally went to the rest room to freshen up. Cara started laughing as soon as they were inside.

"What?" Sally demanded.

"You should have been a snake-oil salesperson. You'd have been a huge success."

"No, thank you. I'm quite successful at selling real estate," Sally replied huffily. Then she spoiled it by laughing. "What a couple of jerks! I don't wish Adam bad luck, but I hope they change their minds about buying the mill. Can you imagine Ted Hardt at a Historical Society meeting?"

Cara sobered. "Adam wants to go back into law. This is his chance to get out from under the obligation he feels toward the town and live his own life."

Sally put her lipstick into her purse and blotted her lips. "The law isn't the only thing he wants." She turned to Cara. "His eyes, when he looks at you... God, if a man ever looked at me like that, I'd die for him."

"He doesn't..." Cara's voice trailed off. There was some truth in Sally's words. Each time she'd met Adam's glance today, spirals of emotion had eddied through her. She felt hopeful, doubtful, happy and sad by turns. Love was confusing.

"Doesn't he?" Sally laughed and gave Cara a wry grimace. "He needs you. Help him realize it. No one can live alone with only a pack of troubles for company for years and years and not crack. Adam may think he's indestructible, but..." She shrugged and opened the door. "I'd like to see you both happy."

Cara squeezed Sally's arm as she went out. "You're a good friend, Winetski," she said in the tough way they'd talked to each other years ago. "If I see anyone who comes close to Adam, I'll send him your way."

"Thanks."

Sally waved goodbye and returned to her office. Cara joined the men for a final tour around the courthouse and a stop at the mayor's office. He took them to the police station to meet the chief. At five they arrived back at the big house. Tea was ready in the conservatory.

"This has been quite a day," Miller decided, expansive after eating the perfect scones—six of them—not to mention being treated like royalty all day. Ted Hardt wore a fatuous grin. He gave Cara a leering wink.

She modestly looked down into her teacup and ignored his heavy-handed flirting. Depression took hold of her spirits. Adam had hated the thought of selling to the conglomerate, now she saw why. These men wouldn't care about the town and its people. Only the bottom line interested them.

"What?"

Hardt was leaning close to her, speaking to her alone. Adam and Miller crossed the room to inspect a flax wheel set up in one corner. She needed to add it to the inventory, she realized.

"I asked if there was any chance you would move

your business here." He made it plain he was interested.

"Oh, uh, no."

"Perhaps we could find you a job in the mill. I'll need a secretary when I move here."

Work for him? That'd be the day. "I'm an expert in my field. Why would I change?"

His eyes flew open. He stole a glance at Adam. "As a...?"

"I evaluate antiques. My family owns Townsend Antique Appraisal and Auction Company," she told him coolly.

Hardt's expression became more respectful. "Are you and Clairmont engaged?"

She smiled. "We've spoken of marriage, yes. But now he has other things occupying his mind. When his business with you is concluded..." She gave a slight shrug.

The awkward conversation ended when the other men returned to their seats at the table. "It's time for you to go if you're to make your connections," Adam reminded his guests. He and Cara walked them to the rental car.

After they said their farewells, Ted Hardt added, "It was nice of your fiancée to devote a day to business. That bodes well for your marriage, don't you think?"

Cara realized the man was taunting her, that he didn't think she and Adam had a serious relationship.

Adam dropped an arm over her shoulders. "Definitely. I don't get to spend near enough time with her, but I'm hoping to change that soon."

When the car drove off, Cara looked up at Adam.

"I didn't tell him we were engaged. He asked about it. I merely said we'd discussed marriage."

"So we have," Adam agreed, his voice dropping to the husky level he'd used that morning when they woke together. "That was a long time ago, Cara."

"I know." She swallowed nervously when he continued gazing into her eyes, his thoughts unreadable. She was suddenly aware of a pulse beating erratically in her temple.

"Do you think we can finish with those transcripts tomorrow? I need to spend Friday in the office."

The hope died and the doubts came whirling back. "Yes, I'm sure we can."

The next day they started early and worked until midnight.

Cara looked at their pitiful list of clues and possibilities. "That's it," she said. "We've covered it all. We...I'm not going to look further."

"Are you sure? We can question Mr. Wagner—"

"No," she said sharply. "I'll not harass that old man for a hopeless cause. It's done. The past is finished."

"And the hurt?"

"I'll always regret what happened to my father, but it's over. I've kept my promise to my mother. I've done my best for him, for his memory." Now she must build some memories of her own, she realized. Her mother had started a new life; it was time she did the same. "I want to go forward."

A blaze leaped into his eyes. She thought he would take her into his arms, but he only nodded. "I think we'd better call it a night. Are you coming to the mill in the morning?"

"I have your father's office to inventory and some final notes to put in my report, then I'll be finished."

"Good. Will you have lunch with me?"

"In the company cafeteria?"

He nodded.

Twice would practically make them engaged in the eyes of the town. "Yes." Neither of them smiled, but she knew it was a beginning. They were starting over.

He kissed her solemnly upon the lips and let her go. She went to bed alone, but she thought it wouldn't be long before they'd be together. Perhaps after the dance tomorrow night.

Definitely after the dance...

Cara drove down the winding road to the mill. The relentless spring rain had produced results. Buds were unfurling with reckless joy on every tree limb. She passed a wild cherry tree in riotous bloom. A few sprays of that in the house would be nice, she decided. She'd pick some on the way home.

Home, she thought. The big house. Home. It sounded right.

At the mill she parked and quickly ran inside. Mrs. Boswell told her to go right up; she'd already unlocked the door to Clayton's old office. Cara thanked her and ran up the steps and along the hall.

The door to Clayton Clairmont's office was oak with three opaque glass panels set into it, a repeat of the three beveled clear panes set into the front door. Feeling that she was entering a mortuary, Cara opened the door and stepped inside the room.

Chills crept over her scalp at the sepulchral quiet. Dust motes flickered in the streams of sunshine coming in around the blinds. She went to the window and pulled the cord, opening the wooden slats so that the light could enter.

She let her gaze drift over the dignified office. She could picture the patrician mill owner at his desk, his long, lean fingers holding a pen, his appearance immaculate.

Unlike Adam, who usually worked in his shirt-sleeves, with his tie loosened and his hair rumpled from running his fingers through it when he became impatient, Clayton had been very conscious of outward appearances.

Warmth stole through her. If nothing else, she at least had an image of Adam to take back with her to Virginia. If nothing happened between them tonight.

She knew his strengths, some of his flaws, most of his mannerisms because of this trip. If she discovered nothing else, her journey hadn't been in vain.

Gathering her wayward thoughts, she went to the first piece of furniture and began examining it. There were more items than she'd expected. Two were valuable antiques. The Toby mugs, circa the Revolutionary War, were a wonderful find.

She opened each drawer and cabinet. As Adam had said, the files had been moved. Everything was empty.

The opening of the door alerted her to Adam's presence. "Hello," he said when she spun around.

"Hi." The word seemed inadequate for the excitement she felt upon seeing him. She rushed on. "You have some good things here. Tiffany lamps, oh, and two Toby mugs."

"What are Toby mugs?" He came in. The door swung closed.

She held up one. "A drinking cup. It holds a pint

of ale. They depict people—a strutting mayor, a merry sailor, a plump goodwife in her apron and cap—a sort of humorous record of the occupations of the time.''

He came to her and examined the mug in detail, tracing the lines of the figurine—which was a carpenter, complete with leather apron and tools—with a fingertip.

"The onyx desk set is in mint condition."

He glanced at the stuff, then handed the mug back to her. When she met his eyes, she saw the hunger in him. Yes, oh, yes, he wanted her!

She acknowledged another emotion in him. Loneliness. He'd been working on the edge, by himself, for years. All the worries and none of the rewards. Mrs. Groves had been right.

She longed to reach up and smooth the errant lock of hair off his forehead. The palms of her hands burned with the need to touch him, to run her hands over him in soothing caresses, to give him release with her body, shared with him in love, with all of love's delight in the giving.

"It's late," he said. "Are you ready for lunch?"

She nodded. Unable to sustain the scrutiny of his heated gaze, she looked away. Surely he could see the yearning in her.

He put a hand under her chin, lifting her face so he could study it. "What is it?"

"You. Me. Us."

He laughed, softly, sexily, and some of the worry lifted from his eyes. "Yes, of course." He walked to the door and held it open. "Are you almost finished in here?''

"I have only the desk left to check." She followed him down the steps.

They were almost the last ones in the cafeteria. During lunch, she felt warmed each time she looked at him. Another, stronger reaction set in. He wanted her, and she wanted him. He'd loved her once. She was almost sure he did now.

"How do you think Miller reacted to the area?" she asked when they finished discussing her project. She knew which of the two men was the important one.

"He liked it well enough. Your emphasis on the loveliness, the peace and quiet, impressed them. Sally's talk about the quality of life—the schools, the lack of drugs and the low crime rate—was also good."

She listened quietly, proud that she had helped. After the meal she returned to Clayton's office with a lighter heart. Somehow she knew it would all work out. It had to. There was passion between them. There had to be love as well.

Looking back with the maturity of eight years to guide her, she realized it had mostly been her pride that hadn't allowed her to listen to Adam. She'd been too young to handle the turmoil of that time and the disgrace her family had suffered.

But now she was older. She understood that the past didn't have to interfere between her and Adam. She had to convince him she believed him. She was ready for his love...at last.

This weekend would be the perfect time to show him just how ready she was. She smiled, then she laughed softly. She hugged herself tightly, holding back all the wild, tumultuous emotion that threatened to cause her to break the bonds of propriety and rush to Adam's office right this minute.

Tonight. After the dance. Oh, yes!

Going to Clayton's desk, she opened the rolltop. It ran smoothly through its tracks. She picked up an onyx inkwell.

After checking it, she listed it on her pad along with the gold pen set with an emerald twinkling on the top. It was the old-fashioned kind that could be refilled. Good. She had a client who collected them.

She opened each drawer. Each was empty.

Sitting in the comfortable executive chair, she ran her fingers along the edge of the desk, which was inlaid with flowers of rosewood, the carvings very deep and ornate. The desk was a beautiful piece of work from a Dutch or English master, she wasn't sure which. Her stepfather was the expert on European stuff.

An odd sensation stopped her when she started to leave. She was finished, but she sat back down and studied the desk. Tingles crept along her nerves. An impulse to explore took hold of her.

She ran her fingertips along the carved edges again. If the desk was the workmanship of a European craftsman, it might have a secret niche. They often incorporated such devices in their work. She couldn't leave until she'd satisfied her curiosity that none existed in this particular one. She dropped to her knees and peered under the center drawer.

The drawer closed firmly against a solid piece of wood at the back. The solid plank formed a smooth surface from the drawer to the back of the carved wood panel that skirted the front side of the desk. A flutter went through her.

Somehow she knew there was a secret drawer. She had an instinct for them and had found several that had even fooled her stepfather. Pulling out each side drawer, she inspected them thoroughly. No discrepancies there. The obvious bottom was the real one. Ditto for the back and sides of each drawer. She checked the inside of the desk. Nothing there.

Except that unexpected piece of wood behind the center drawer.

It didn't support a drawer guide; those were along the sides. She removed the drawer entirely and tapped on the piece. There was no hollow sound, but she wasn't convinced.

She began a methodical search of the entire desk. On a scroll along the right front portion, she found what she was looking for.

By pushing on the center of the scroll, it acted like a tiny release bar. The front of the seemingly solid piece of wood swung free. Cara pressed her hands together. Then, holding her breath, she pulled the tiny door open. Inside was a paper.

She withdrew a manila envelope, one with a metal clasp. The flap wasn't glued down. She let her breath out with a whoosh.

Chiding herself for being melodramatic, she opened the clasp and took out two sheets of paper.

"Adam," the letter began, "my dear son."

She'd found it. Clayton's confession. She skimmed it quickly and began to look at it more closely.

The office door opened. Adam came in.

Chapter Nine

"Cara?"

Cara thrust the envelope and letter into the compartment and closed the panel. Oh, God, she couldn't face him. He would see that something was wrong. She was shaking. Calm, she had to be calm. Breathe deeply. Again. She forced her muscles to relax.

"Cara?" A note of concern crept into Adam's voice.

"Here," she called, hoping he wouldn't notice the tremor in hers. She had to get rid of him. She needed to be alone, to collect her thoughts. She had to reread the letter in its entirety and make sure it said what she'd thought on first skimming it.

"What are you doing, playing hide-and-seek?" he demanded, amused as she crawled from under the desk.

She tried to think of a retort, but her mind wasn't up to it at the moment. "Did you want something?" she asked.

The laughter left his eyes at her curt question. "Your mother called. The intercom doesn't seem to be working in here, so I told her you'd call back."

He picked up the telephone. Cara heard the dial tone come on. Adam pushed the button for the intercom. Nothing.

"Well, the main line is working. You can call her from here." He gave her a curious glance. "How's it going?"

"Fine. Actually, I'm finished." She replaced the drawer in the desk, then looked at him with her hand on the phone, making it clear she expected him to leave. "Thanks for the message."

"Anytime." He turned and walked out.

She slumped into the executive chair. A close call. She wasn't ready to disclose her discovery. First she had to absorb its meaning herself and decide what to do with it. People's lives would be changed.

She should have felt elation at reaching her goal, but she realized her foremost thought was for Adam. He would be hurt. Once she'd thought she wouldn't care, but now she admitted she did. She cared very much.

You made a promise, her conscience reminded her. *You can't withhold the truth. Justice must be done.*

Why? her heart asked. *After all this time, why hurt more people? Why hurt Adam?*

It was like being eighteen again, her life and her heart torn apart by circumstances she didn't control. Except this time she did. The choices were all hers.

Tremors started from deep inside her, like the faint warnings before the volcano erupted. When she released this news, it would blow Adam's life apart.

She closed her eyes. Heaven help her, she couldn't think what to do.

After a few minutes she called her mother. The sound of that familiar loving voice nearly made her break down and weep.

"Some of your friends called and wanted to know when you were coming home. They're planning something, a dinner or party, for Saturday night. What should I tell them?" her mother asked after their greeting.

Cara couldn't face the thought of a party. "Tell them thanks, but I won't be able to make this one. Is that all? I...I need to get back to work. I want to finish up...as soon as possible."

"When will you be home?"

"Probably Sunday." She would leave tomorrow, but she wanted Saturday alone at her apartment to think.

"Good. We've missed you."

"I've missed you, too. And Thomas." Her voice wavered. She cleared her throat. "Mom?"

"Yes?"

She wanted to confess her find, but she couldn't. She wanted to ask her mother's advice. She couldn't do that, either. This was a decision she had to make alone—whether to vindicate her and her mother's faith in her father or to destroy Adam's life.

"Nothing," she said. Her voice came out a croak. She cleared it again. "I'd better get back to work. I have a report..." She let the sentence trail off.

"Are you all right, Cara?" her mother asked on a note of worry. "You aren't sick, are you?"

"No, of course not. I'm fine."

"You haven't found anything...interesting, have you?"

"No, just...just the stuff that was always here, some really valuable pieces, the Marie Antoinette opera glasses and the Martha Washington dining-room suite. I haven't told Adam how valuable Thomas thinks it might be," she chattered brightly.

They talked a few more minutes about auctioning the pieces. Cara hung up. A fine sweat had broken out all over her. She felt feverish and ill. Think! She had to think. What should she do?

There was no way she could decide at that moment. She needed to read the letter, slowly this time, and absorb the impact of it. She reached for the scroll.

Footsteps sounded along the hall. Cara drew back.

Mrs. Boswell stuck her head in the door. She gave Cara an inquisitive glance when she saw her sitting in the chair, doing nothing. "I've a free moment. Do you have the inventory ready for this room? I'll type it and the final draft of your report."

Cara stood, picked up her purse and papers and joined the secretary in the hall. "Here it is. I want to add a few notes on the report before you redo it, if you don't mind."

"Not at all. With the computer it's easy to make changes. I used to hate for anyone to mark on a page after I'd typed it once, but now it's no problem."

They talked of modern technology on the way down. An hour later, after Cara turned in her official report and the attached inventory, she had no excuse for staying. Reluctantly she left the building and went to the van, which held two spinning wheels and several iron pots and kettles she'd bought during short excursions into the countryside during the past two weeks.

Driving out of the parking lot, she headed for the bluff overlooking the town. Once there, she got out of the van and sat on a boulder near the edge, staring down at the town. When she left, she knew she'd never come back.

She looked at the sky. Empty. She hadn't seen any hawks returning to nest this year. Neither would she.

Grief tore through her soul like lightning through a pine, exploding the foolishly revived dreams, burning them right to the ground. She should have known better.

Romeo and Juliet hadn't been able to survive their families' enmity. The love between her and Adam wouldn't either.

She saw the dilemma clearly.

If she disclosed Clayton's confession, Adam would be hurt beyond repair. He had been angry and disbelieving when she listed his father as a suspect. He'd cast the notion aside as absurd. His father would never have allowed himself to gamble his life away or be involved in a sex scandal.

He hadn't. *He'd taken the money to save the mill and the town.* Noblesse oblige. Or perhaps family pride. It would be a blow to the ego to be the one to close the doors forever on a company your family had kept going for generations.

Mr. Clairmont had known he was dying. He had thought he could save the mill and thus the town, and the money would be repaid out of his life insurance, which was a large amount. But he'd died before he could execute all his plans and make sure Adam knew about the letter.

Adam's mother, the sole beneficiary, had taken the insurance money and gone to live in Florida, away from a place she'd never particularly liked. Putting all the pieces together, Cara realized Mrs. Clairmont, a Miami debutante, had stayed because she loved her husband, but her roots had been far from here. Cara couldn't fault the woman for going home.

So where did that leave her and Adam?

If she didn't tell him about the letter, if they fell in love again and married and *then* the letter came to light...what would that do to them?

Or worse, she might blurt out her secret in the midst of a quarrel. Adam would hate her if she withheld the truth and he found out later.

No, her heart assured, *she'd never tell.*

But she knew human nature. She wasn't a saint. Her feelings for her own family were strong. Even if she kept the secret, the knowledge of the injustice might eat at her like a cancer, filling her with resentment that *her* family had suffered for *his* father's sins. That would destroy their marriage, leaving them both bitter, except Adam would never know the cause of it, only the frustration of not knowing why they were growing apart. She couldn't bear the thought of exchanging bitterness for love. She couldn't!

She closed her eyes, wishing for the release of tears, but none would come. It was too late, much too late, for tears.

There was only the future to be faced. Alone. In time, Paradise Falls and Adam, her first love, would fade into the mists of memory. Like Adam had said— a Brigadoon, gone forever.

But she would never forget, not entirely.

She stared at the town, glistening in the afternoon

sun, a long shadow of mountain peak beginning to darken the western edge, as if its disappearance had already begun.

Anguish shrieked through her, a dark, lonesome thing. She drew her knees up and huddled tightly into herself, fighting it, knowing her decision had been made.

Adam, my love, my never-forgotten love.

"Adam will be late," Mrs. Groves advised when Cara walked into the kitchen at dusk.

"Did he say we were still going to the dance?" Cara asked. She had to get through the evening as best she could.

"Yes. He'll be home in time for that. Be ready to leave at eight, he said." Mrs. Groves indicated the oven. "Your supper is ready. I'm going to baby-sit for my daughter. She and her husband are attending, too. The proceeds will go toward new equipment for the science room at the high school."

"I'll look forward to meeting her," Cara said.

She dawdled until the housekeeper left in her subcompact car, then had a glass of milk. She turned off the oven and set the quiche out to cool. She didn't think she could force food past her aching throat.

In her room she quickly showered and changed into a simple black dress with long sleeves and a modest neckline. She added the pearls. With the portentous calm of the emotionally exhausted, she put on her makeup. Adam arrived home just as she went down.

He paused at the bottom of the steps. His eyes feasted on her. She returned his gaze. She realized it was the last night she'd have with him.

"I'll be ready in fifteen minutes," he said.

She recognized the slight rasp of passion in his voice, in the way it deepened as he devoured her with a glance. She nodded, not trusting her voice, and went on into the library when he dashed down the hall to his room. She thought of the photo album in the Hepplewhite secretary and wondered if it was the one Mrs. Groves had told her about, the one filled with pictures of her.

He'd loved her deeply then. Perhaps... No. She would dream useless dreams no more. She'd made her decision.

The letter must be destroyed. Only then could the past stay decently buried. Enough people had been hurt. She couldn't bring herself to stir it all up again.

Adam had once cherished her. She couldn't bear the thought of his hating her when she exposed the truth. Neither could she face the fear that her feelings for him might change if she stayed with him after suppressing the facts. That was the crux of her despair.

"Ready?"

She jerked and whirled about. Adam stood in the doorway, lean and handsome in a dark suit. He smiled at her. Her heart skipped several beats.

"Nervous about tonight? It'll just be us homefolks."

His gaze was tender. She saw an awareness of them, as a couple, as lovers, in his eyes. Quick, hot desire washed over her, but it couldn't touch the ice that had formed around her heart.

"I know," she said. She picked up her purse from the tavern sofa where she'd entertained many erotic images of them and had known the actuality of his embrace. She wished they'd made love.

On the trip down the mountain, he told her about some of the people she'd known. "Were you in school with Johnny Jackson?"

"Yes."

"He's circuit court clerk now."

"Really? Will wonders never cease," she said.

Adam cast Cara a quick glance before swinging left into the parking lot at the inn. She was the only female he'd ever been in tune with, and he sensed something troubling her. There was a sadness in her. She looked at the passing scenery as if she were saying goodbye.

A fist clutched something vital in his chest. He knew then that he didn't want her to leave, not ever. He sucked in a harsh breath. There was no reason they couldn't go forward. The past was dead. All that was left was them and their new, growing feelings for each other.

"Some wonders never will," he said a minute later when he helped her from his car. He caressed her arm. She looked away. He tried to tamp down the rampant hunger he knew must be reflected on his face. Later, after the dance...

The dance was already in progress when they arrived. He paid the entrance fee, and they went to find a table. He saw Sally Winetski on the floor, wearing three-inch heels and standing four inches taller than her partner. He chuckled.

Cara looked up at him.

"Sally," he explained. "She's not shy about her height. I've always admired her spunk and ambition."

"Yes, she's been the same since I've known her."

Sally called to them. "I've saved two places." She pointed out the table.

Cara was grateful they'd be in company. Adam wasn't bothering to conceal his attraction to her. When he looked at her, she felt vulnerable. He wanted her, and heaven knew she wanted him. It wasn't meant to be, but Adam didn't know that yet.

"White wine?" he asked, bending close so that his breath stroked her cheek.

Nodding, she chose a seat and sat down before her knees gave way. His nearness was making her weak.

She looked over the crowd, not recognizing anyone but Sally of the younger set. Of the older adults, she saw Miss Josie and Mr. Wagner. They were dancing with the camaraderie of old friends.

She watched them, then turned away as tears formed. Now was not the time. The tune ended and Sally came over, her escort in tow. Adam returned. After the introductions, Sally motioned for Cara to come with her. She introduced her to Betty, who was Mrs. Groves's daughter.

"I wanted to thank you for the advice," Betty said. "It never occurred to me that corn could cause any problem, but it was the skin. Baby food is mashed and strained until the babies are old enough to handle the added fiber."

They talked for a few minutes more, laughing when Sally recounted a tale of her nephew finding a nice kitty. "One with a white stripe down its back," she finished. "They had to drive with the car windows down through all of winter and most of spring."

A hand settled on Cara's shoulder. "I think it's my turn."

Cara couldn't keep hold of her smile when Adam took her to the dance floor and encircled her with both hands around her waist. She laid her hands on his shoulders. He pulled her solidly against him when she would have held her distance.

"What was so funny?" he asked, a smidgen of jealousy evident in the question.

Yesterday she would have thrilled to hear it. "Babies and children," she replied.

"Babies," he repeated. His eyes never left hers.

Tears, hot, angry, despairing, pushed against her eyes. They would never have the children they'd talked about.

"They're a lot of trouble." She managed a laugh. "Oh, there's Linda, Sally's sister. She's still beautiful. Sally and I were so envious of her while we were growing up."

"You don't have to envy anyone."

She felt her lips tremble and knew she wasn't going to be able to control her emotions very long. "Spoken like a true gallant." The words didn't come out as teasing as she'd planned.

He frowned. "What's wrong with you tonight?"

"Nothing. Why?"

"You're acting funny...brittle, like some society female at a charity ball. Are we yokels boring you?"

Adam smiled, but his question was serious. If she disliked the town, she wouldn't be happy living here. His mother had never particularly liked it, but she'd loved his father enough to stay. Cara had never shown that kind of love for him.

Be fair, his conscience ordered. *She was only eighteen.*

"No," she said in reply.

He wasn't a fool. He knew when a woman was withdrawing. The problem was to discover why. He muttered a savage curse and pulled her deeper into his embrace so that their thighs touched. He was hard and aching for her. She was cool and distant with him.

When the number ended, Cara fled from Adam's arms. At their table she talked with old school chums, including Johnny Jackson. He was skinny, wore glasses and had lost most of his hair. She would never have recognized him on the street.

Adam...she would have known him anywhere, no matter how long it had been since they'd last met, she realized. Like the hawks returning from their solitary winter quarters, she'd have known her true mate when they met again.

She studied him while he talked. He would be handsome into old age. There was a quiet strength in him that molded his face into firm lines and his shoulders into a proud bearing. He had inherited his father's patrician manners, but with an extra dab of friendliness thrown in. The local people liked him.

He turned his head and looked at her, his gaze now wary. The hunger was still there, but he'd banked it somewhat. During the dance she'd felt his reaction to her, his body urgent and hungry against hers. If they made love...

She couldn't bear to think of it. If she did anything so foolish, it would be that much harder to leave.

She danced with Johnny and Mr. Wagner and several others. By midnight her face was stiff from smiling. How much longer?

Adam frowned at her when they met at their table after exchanging partners with the mayor and his wife. "I think it's time I took you home."

"Yes."

Sally protested. "I thought we'd go to the diner for a quiet chat after the dance."

"Cara has been working hard all week," Adam explained. He knew something was wrong. Cara had been play-acting all night, her smiles as fake as a three-dollar bill.

It took another half hour for him to get her out of the room. Everyone told her how glad they were that she'd come. Finally he escorted her to the Porsche and tucked her in. The wind off the mountain was gentle but cold. She folded her arms as if closing herself in...and him out.

He drove to the house in silence and went straight to the underground garage instead of letting her out the door.

"There are things down here," she said, looking around the huge basement area on the way to the steps. "You should have told me. I can check them—"

"It's all lawn furniture or junk. You can look it over at some later date," he said.

He led her into the house and down the hall. She balked at the stairs, refusing to follow him into the library.

"I want to go to my room. I'm terribly tired," she said.

Frustration ate at him. He ran a hand through his hair, sweeping back the annoying strand that fell over his forehead. Recognizing the impatient gesture, he dropped his hand to his side. "What's going on?"

He watched her lick her lips and wanted to kiss her until she melted. Then he would take her to his room and make love to her all night, for the rest of their lives. Yeah, that's what he wanted.

"What do you mean?" She turned half away from

him as if she intended to bound up the stairs any second.

"Quit stalling." He caught her shoulders and turned her to face him. "I thought things were different between us. Yesterday and last night, you looked at me...hell, you gave me a come-on a blind man would have noticed. Today it's the cold shoulder. What gives with you?"

She gave him one of those blank female glances that pretended she didn't know what he meant. Frustration climbed another notch.

"Dammit, Cara—"

"Let me go, Adam."

The quiet cold of her voice was the final straw. He swept her to him. He'd thaw her out, then he'd discover why she was shutting him out of her life... again.

Cara couldn't breathe. Adam ravaged her mouth ruthlessly, refusing to release her or let her catch a breath. She moaned as needs too long suppressed leaped to life. His hands—his wonderful hands—stroked her back from her neck to her waist and beyond. He cupped her hips and held her while he moved against her in a way that left no doubt of his desire.

She jerked her head to the side. "Adam, don't."

He buried his face in her neck, leaving a stinging path of kisses there. "I can't help it. One look, one taste, and I have to have more. Stay with me tonight," he coaxed.

"I can't."

"Yes." He slid his hands around her and cupped her breasts, holding them like precious treasures while he sought her mouth. "Kiss me," he demanded. He made a soft, low sound in the back of his throat. "Let me love you, Cara. Help me wipe out all those long, lonely nights when I dreamed of you."

"Adam, please, don't," she begged, evading his lips. Her will was weakening. "Let me go."

"I should have made love to you last night. You were ready then," he murmured, kissing the corner of her mouth.

"No."

He ignored her. "But I didn't want our first time to be with those two jerks in the house. I wanted privacy, lots of it."

"No," she whispered again. She arched her head back, defying him. His warmth invaded her body, making her want to yield.

"Why?" He stared into her eyes with all the force of an outraged male who had reached the limits.

"Because..." She drew a shaky breath. "Because I'm asking you to."

He released her. They stood an inch apart, both panting slightly. When he spoke, there was finality in his voice.

"I'm asking you to come to my room with me. Right now."

"Adam, I can't."

"I'm asking you to marry me, to live with me here in this house, forever perhaps, or until I get things resolved, then to go with me wherever the future takes us."

She stared at him. Heaven, he offered her heaven. And she had to refuse. She shook her head.

"I love you."

She was silent.

"You love me."

At last she spoke. "Not enough."

It was like watching the sun blink out. His eyes went dark. "I guess that says it all." He turned and walked out the front door and out of her life.

She ran to her room and locked the door. Then, unable to help herself, she went to the window. In the pale wash of moonlight, she saw him walking along the road, his hands in his pockets—a man rejected...a man alone.

While tears coursed down her face, she packed. Before light appeared beyond the ridge, she climbed into the van and started the engine. A little later she stopped on the bluff.

There was no fog to shroud the little valley tucked under the protective peaks. It lay open and vulnerable to her gaze. Her greatest happiness and her greatest sorrow had occurred there. Dreams had been born and dreams had died there. It would happen again and again, she mused. As long as there were people, as long as there was love.

Adam, my love, goodbye.

Chapter Ten

Cara crawled into bed when she reached her apartment and fell asleep at once. It was late in the afternoon before she woke to the sound of the telephone ringing.

She hesitated, then let it ring. The answering machine got it. She heard her mother's voice.

"Cara? I saw the van at your place when I went to the grocery. Call me when it's convenient."

She burrowed deeper into the pillow. She didn't want to talk to anyone. Neither her mind nor her body felt rested. If she could only sleep a hundred years, then none of this would matter.

But once awake, the memories rushed upon her. With a restlessness she couldn't control, she flung out of bed and into the shower. Later, dressed in a fleecy jogging outfit, she listened to her phone messages. The first was from a friend who was having a party. She ignored it.

Sighing, she listened to the rest of the recording, then called her mother. "Mom, it's Cara."

"I'm glad you made it back safely. I was worried about those roads. Did you have a good trip?"

Had she made it back safely? Not quite, not if you counted a broken heart as a tragedy. "Yes, the trip was fine. I've...I've always loved the mountains."

"I know."

Her mother's tone was one of understanding, and Cara wondered how much her mother had guessed about Adam and her.

"I got in this morning. I've been asleep." She couldn't think of anything to say. "Oh, I picked up a couple of spinning wheels and some iron pots."

"Cara, are you all right?"

Her throat closed, and she couldn't speak for a moment. "Yes, I...it was..."

"Perhaps I shouldn't have let you go to Paradise Falls alone," her mother fretted. "I know how deeply you felt the humiliation when your father was arrested."

"No more than you or Dad."

Her mother sighed. "I'd hoped... Cara, this may seem odd, coming so late, but I think you need to put the past behind and...and get on with your life."

Was her mother encouraging her to return to Adam? If only she could. "I think you may be right," she said with as much cheer as she could muster. "Anyway, that's exactly what I intend to do from this moment forward."

"Good."

Cara wiped at the tears that rolled down her cheeks. It was a good thing she was on the phone, else she'd never have been able to carry off this farce.

"Thomas and I talked about it after the last time you called. We think you should expand your horizons. How does a trip to Europe sound?"

A chance to be alone and let her heart mend without having to maintain a cheerful facade before her family and friends? She'd take it. "That sounds wonderful. How much would it cost?"

"The company would pay your expenses. You need to go to the museums and learn to recognize the different styles."

Cara knew where the suggestion came from and was touched. "Tell Thomas that's very generous of him, but I feel I should pay half my way."

"Then it's all settled. We'll make arrangements to plan the itinerary Monday when you come in."

Cara smiled in spite of her tears. Her mother was all for getting started once a decision had been made. "All right, but I have some things to do. We'll need to arrange for a truck to pick up the furniture Adam wants to sell."

"Did he agree to let the Martha Washington suite go?"

"Yes, also the opera glasses and...and his father's office furniture as well as a few other items."

"Good," her mother said. "We already have a client who's interested in the dining suite. Mrs. Liverpool heard Thomas talking to the New York auction house yesterday and demanded first chance at it. He explained the bidding floor would start at half a million. She's willing to pay whatever it takes."

"A half million," Cara murmured on a gasping breath. She'd known it was worth a lot, but that much? "Mom, would you ask Thomas to call Adam and tell him that?"

"Well, yes, of course."

Cara was thankful her mother didn't ask her why she didn't make the call, although she could hear the question in her voice.

"What are you doing tomorrow? Do you want to go to an estate sale with us?"

"No, I need to wash clothes and air out the apartment, but thanks, anyway."

After they said goodbye, Cara contemplated what her decision would mean to her mother. If she ever found out Cara had hidden the truth because of Adam, would she ever forgive her?

But she'll never find out, Cara reminded herself. As soon as the desk arrived, she would destroy the letter from Clayton, and that would be the end of it. Without that bit of evidence, no one could prove anything.

After a busy day of putting her apartment in order and shopping for groceries, Cara went to work Monday in a quiet mood. She arranged for the shipment of Adam's furniture with their most trusted driver. Then she and her mother looked at travel brochures. The week crept by, busy but slow.

On Friday she waited, her heart lurching each time someone came into the office, where she checked the inventory against the price listings to make sure she'd quoted them correctly. At last the truck pulled into the courtyard shortly after lunch.

"Over there, Ben," she directed, going outside. "We have a special warehouse ready for this load. Did you have any trouble coming down the mountain?"

The burly driver grinned. "It was one son-of-a-gun

road, that one, but I made it okay. Clairmont came along," he added.

Without saying more, he walked off toward the back of the truck and began giving instructions to the men who were to unload the big van. Cara froze when a car pulled from behind the truck and parked in front of the office. Adam climbed out.

"Adam!" Her voice was a sharp gasp.

"Hello. I didn't mean to shock you," he apologized while coming up the steps. When he stood beside her, he continued, "I thought I'd come and see how fast we could move this sale along. Thomas wants everything to go to auction, but I thought I'd talk to Mrs. Liverpool about the Washington furniture."

"Oh. Oh, yes, of course."

He gave her a grin, inviting her to join in. "Do you realize what this means?" he demanded. She shook her head. "That furniture is the down payment on a whole new line of equipment. I can tell the conglomerate to take a flying leap...in polite terms, of course." He laughed.

She managed a croak of merriment. Mentally she stumbled over the implications of his arrival. Didn't he trust her to handle the sale of his property? Or did he suspect her of something else?

She was so unnerved by his presence that the most insensitive person on earth would immediately be put on guard by her breathless mumbling. Trying for composure, she gestured toward the door.

"Won't you come in? I was just going over the prices for some of the office furniture." She led the way inside.

Her mother looked up.

"Mother, you remember Adam Clairmont, don't you?"

"Of course." Her mother stood and held out a hand. "I'm glad to see you again, Adam."

He shook hands. "Thank you, Mrs. Gardner...but it's Townsend now, isn't it?" he corrected.

"Please, call me Ann."

Cara watched the other two look each other over. Her mother had no ill feelings toward Adam apparently. Her manner was open and friendly. She invited him to have dinner with them.

"Thomas will be back by six. I know he'll want to discuss the auction with you. Can you stay?"

"I'd hoped you would ask." His smile was charming and without guile. "I'm here mostly out of curiosity. I wanted to see your operation and ask if the proceedings can be hurried. I'm...anxious to resolve some issues."

"Well, we don't want to rush things. We have to plan an advertising campaign and all that," her mother explained. "I'm sure you want to get the top price."

"Definitely."

He cast Cara a glance that she couldn't read. She didn't need overt signs to be suspicious, though. She felt vibrations passing from him to her. There was a determination in his manner that worried her. Why had he come?

She turned from his narrowed gaze to watch the men moving his furniture into the air-conditioned warehouse. They loaded a desk onto a dolly and wheeled it inside.

Her insides tightened into knots. She wanted to retrieve the letter, burn it and be done with the whole affair. Fate, like a sharpened ax in a madman's hands, arched over her head. She didn't know when it might fall.

A fit of desperation seized her. She put her hand on the door. "I have to check something."

Her mother glanced at her in surprise as Cara butted into the middle of their conversation, but Cara had no time for niceties. She had to get that letter!

"I'll go with you," Adam said.

Frustration built into a scream inside her. She pressed her lips together and nodded. She and Adam went to the warehouse and watched the unloading of the furniture. The expensive pieces had been crated. She checked each crate as it was put into place to see what it contained. The rolltop desk was in one of those. She would have to make up some excuse to open it.

"It's more than I realized," Adam said.

He stood beside her, his forehead furrowed into a frown. The shipping foreman handed her the bill of lading after the men finished. She looked it over. "Well, looks like everything arrived in one piece."

"Yes," Adam agreed.

Cara's heart went out to him. When she risked a glance at him, she found his gaze upon her. For a brief agonizing ten seconds, they stared at each other, a silent exchange of questions overlaid with longing.

"Are you sure you want to get rid of the furniture? It's been in your family so long—"

"Yes," he said, watching her with a questioning expression. "The decision has been made. I won't go back on it."

The arrival of a van, similar to hers, broke the tense moment. Thomas Townsend had returned from his errands. Cara led Adam off the loading ramp to the parking lot to meet her stepfather.

After formally introducing the men, they returned to the office where Adam and Thomas planned an ad campaign. "We'll list the auction as an estate sale. That brings out a lot of people."

"Curiosity," Adam said. "Everyone wants to see who's down on their luck."

"Yes," Thomas agreed. "Or what the ungrateful children are doing with the family heirlooms."

Adam smiled wryly. "I hadn't thought of that."

Cara listened impatiently to the conversation. She wanted to get to the warehouse. Every moment seemed fraught with the danger that someone would beat her to the letter. Which was ridiculous. Only she knew about it.

"Well, shall we go home?" Ann asked later in the afternoon. "We'll grill chicken before it gets dark."

"Won't you let me take you out?" Adam asked. "I don't want to put you to any trouble."

"Yes, why don't we go out?" Cara jumped in. A family dinner was too painful.

"It's no bother," her mother insisted.

"Adam and I'll do the cooking," Thomas stated.

At the house they all went straight to the kitchen. Thomas and her mother accepted Adam as a friend, rather than as a guest who was also a valuable client.

Cara volunteered to prepare the salad while her mother put the meat into a marinade to soak. Adam and Thomas grabbed a beer and went to the back patio to start the coals.

This is what we could have had, she thought, a family meal, just the four of us. Later there would have been children.

She couldn't bear to think about it.

"Cara? You're awfully quiet."

"Just...thinking."

"Perhaps I shouldn't have invited Adam here," her mother said softly. "I know you two once cared for each other. Seeing him must remind you of the bad times."

Cara couldn't reply. Her feelings must be obvious. She would have to do better or Adam would demand to know why she was throwing away this second chance for their happiness.

Her mother spoke again. "Can't you put the past behind you and start over?"

She shook her head. "It's too late," she murmured in a tight voice.

"Oh, honey, I'm sorry." Her mother squeezed her shoulder and let her go. "Your father and I sometimes forgot how hard all this was on you. We were so wrapped in our own misery, we neglected to stop and think about how you were feeling. It's as if we think the young don't feel things as deeply."

Cara managed a smile. "I survived. We all did. Life turned out well here in Virginia, so what have we to complain about?"

Her mother didn't look convinced at her bright tone, but before she could say more, the men returned.

"The fire is ready, woman," Thomas declared on his usual jovial note. "Where's the beef?"

"It's chicken," her mother said crisply.

Thomas raised his eyebrows at Adam. "Women," he complained. "We eat so much fish and fowl in this house, a man is apt to grow gills and feathers."

"So stop squawking and start cooking," Ann advised without a trace of compassion.

The men laughed and, carrying the platter of meat, went outside to the grill. When the food was ready, everyone helped carry the plates and utensils to the table. Cara mostly listened as the discussion ranged over the pitfalls of the antique market and the problems of the mill with international competition. By the time Adam rose to leave, the two men had resolved most of the world's problems and were on the best fishing spots.

When Adam said good-night, Cara did, too. Once outside, Adam walked her to her car and opened the door for her.

"Shall we go someplace for a nightcap?" he asked.

There was no moon and the streetlight was shaded by the big oak at the corner of the yard. She couldn't read his expression, but his mood seemed introspective. If she stayed near him much longer, she would succumb to temptation and ask him to her place.

"I think not."

He watched her warily, his eyes narrowed. Did he suspect anything? He shrugged. "Well then, good night." There was no mistaking the ice.

"Good night, Adam." She hesitated. "Will you be leaving in the morning?"

"Probably." He walked to the Porsche and climbed in.

She waited until he was gone before she backed the van and started for her apartment. Halfway there, she changed her mind.

Turning around in a side street, she headed for the warehouse. She had a key. What better time to take care of the letter?

Clandestine acts should be done at clandestine hours, she mused when she pulled into the parking lot and stopped. The office building and warehouses had a forlorn atmosphere in the harsh glow of a mercury lamp. She didn't let herself think of anyone lurking in the deep shadows as she crossed the paved courtyard to the warehouse holding Adam's treasures.

After two tries she got the key in the lock and turned it. Quickly she flicked off the burglar alarm and alerted the guard service that she was on the premises. Picking up a crowbar, she went to the crate holding the rolltop desk.

Soon she had it open.

Her nerves jangled with the shrill urgency of an unanswered phone ringing in the night. After removing the middle drawer, she dropped to her knees.

With a trembling hand, she fumbled for the scroll. The lever clicked and the hidden compartment swung open. She removed the letter and, settling back on her heels, read it once more.

Adam, my dear son.
By the time you read this letter, I will be gone. I apologize for leaving my business affairs in disorder. You alone will have to sort them out. Your mother has never been interested in the mill, and so will not be able to help you. This is what I would prefer to be done, but of course you must do as you think best, given the circumstances. Looking back, I think I made the wrong decision, but it is too late now.

Cara read it to the end. Clayton was as meticulous regarding his death as he'd been in his life. He detailed each item and how it was to be handled, if possible. His concern for his wife brought a flood of fresh tears to Cara's eyes. Like the son, the father had cherished the woman he'd loved.

To be loved like that for all of one's life...

She wiped the tears away and searched her purse for a book of matches. "Damn," she cursed aloud when she failed to find any.

Getting to her feet, she went to the shipping foreman's desk, which was a pack rat's nest, and sifted through the debris on it. Then, finding the drawers unlocked, she looked through them.

A sense of panic gnawed at her. She wanted to hurry, to be done with the deed. At last she found a matchbook from a nearby restaurant in the back of one drawer.

Feeling like the villain in a melodrama, she tore off one match. She checked the wastebasket. It was clean. All she needed was to set off the sprinkler system and have to explain to her folks and the police what she was doing in the warehouse, at twenty past eleven, burning trash.

Tremors raced over her as she struck the match. It went out. She cursed it, the matchmaker and her own shaky hands, and tried again. This time she was successful. Picking up the letter and holding it over the trash can, she brought the match to the lower corner of the paper.

A hand reached past her and snatched the sheets before they could catch fire. "I'll take those," Adam said.

Cara shrieked and whirled. "Adam! What are you doing here?"

"I might ask you the same." He gave her a grim smile after glancing at the letter opening. "But I think I know."

Reality set in and desperation took hold of her. "Give me that." She lunged for the letter.

Adam easily evaded her. He locked one arm around her waist, holding her pinned to him. With the other hand, he held the letter well out of her reach. "I think not. It'll be safer in my hands. Destroying evidence is a crime," he reminded her.

"Adam, please give it to me. It's not what you think," she lied, panting in her effort to be free. "It...it isn't anything."

"No? It has my name on it. Opening other people's mail is also an offense. Be still," he ordered sharply as she struggled against him.

They stood there a timeless second, heart pounding against heart, their eyes, their lips, only inches apart. Then he let her go and stepped out of reach.

He skimmed the letter. "Was this all?"

She nodded.

"There was no envelope?"

She handed it over.

He placed the letter in it. He studied her for another long breath of time, then he turned and left.

"Adam, where are you going?" she cried after him.

He paused at the warehouse door. She saw it was partially open and realized she must have forgotten to close it securely behind her in her anxiety to retrieve the damning letter. Adam had followed her inside with no trouble at all.

"What are you going to do?" she asked more calmly.

He looked back at her. "Whatever is right," he said at last. Then he left.

Chapter Eleven

Cara read the weekly paper from Paradise Falls when it arrived at the office. There was nothing of interest to her in it. She realized the paper was almost a week old by the time they received it in the mail.

Remembering how she'd felt when her father was accused of being dishonest, she worried about Adam. To have the proof of his father's guilt even if it had been done for a noble reason, and knowing his father had let another man carry the blame for years, must cut to the very quick of Adam's soul. She'd wanted so badly to protect him from that.

The following week, on one of those perfect mornings in May when birds sang, flowers nodded on the breeze and the sun caressed the earth with loving fingers of light, she received a special-delivery envelope.

There was no note, only the front-page article of the *Paradise Falls Clarion*. The headline was in bold, two-inch print: EIGHT-YEAR-OLD CRIME SOLVED.

Cara read the article, which occupied most of the front page. All the old coverage of the embezzlement scandal had been dredged up. She saw pictures of her parents, hands clasped, her father looking grim and haggard, her mother gentle and supportive.

There was one of herself on the courthouse steps, her chin lifted defiantly while she stared straight into the camera.

A door to memory opened. The pain rolled out, smashing everything in its path—her young dreams, the wonder of love, the future she and Adam had planned.

Adam was hurting like that—

"Cara, what is it? What has happened?"

Cara stared at her mother through a haze. The tears spilled over. "Adam," she said hoarsely, shoving the paper at her mother. "Mother, it's Adam."

Thomas, his expression full of concern, handed Cara his handkerchief, and then read the article over his wife's shoulder. When they finished, her mother was also weeping. Cara filled them in on the whole story.

"At last," Ann said, "at last, Stephen will be cleared. The article says the case will be reviewed tomorrow. Adam will submit the letter as new evidence. Stephen will be cleared!" She clung to her husband and sobbed with joy. Thomas held her and ran a soothing hand down her hair. There were tears in his eyes, too.

The scene was tender. It brought fresh pain to Cara

as memory stirred again. She and her mother and father had had each other during those dark days of long ago. "Adam has no one to stand by him," she realized. "We had each other, but Adam has no one."

Ann wiped her tears. Sympathy came into her eyes as she and Thomas watched Cara. "You'll have to go to him," she said.

"I turned away from him, all those years ago, and…and at his house…after I found the letter. I didn't think there was a chance for us.…"

"You were young. He'll understand. Go to him."

Cara looked at her mother, into eyes that were nearly a match of her own. Understanding flowed between them. When Stephen had needed her, his wife had stood by him. Now she was urging her daughter to do the same for the man she loved.

"I…I don't know." Adam might turn away from her.

"If you love him, go to him," her mother said.

Cara looked at her stepfather. "I have an auction scheduled."

"Your mother and I can handle it. Take all the time you need," he encouraged.

She looked from one to the other, loving them, then kissed them both before rushing to her van and hurrying home.

At her apartment she showered and dressed in slacks and a blouse for the trip. In thirty minutes she was packed and on her way to the mountains of West Virginia.

The hours on the road passed in a blur. She rehearsed several opening lines, but none seemed to express what she wanted to say. At Vista Point, she glanced briefly at the town lying in the secluded valley. It gleamed like a fairyland in the twilight. A ground fog drifted near the river.

A hawk rode a thermal, high overhead. She watched it for a minute. Another joined it. They dived and rose on the wind. A male and female, she realized, returning home to mate and raise their young. She watched until they disappeared over the far peak, hoping this was an omen of luck for her.

Determination displaced fear. She, too, was returning to her rightful mate. She knew that now.

Putting the van into a lower gear, she followed the road over the ridge and into town. The mill was dark when she drove past it. She continued up the road to the big house. It, too, was dark. It occurred to her that Adam might be out of town.

He could have left for good. After turning over the evidence to the county prosecutor's office, he could have washed his hands of the case and left to begin a new life away from scandal...away from memories. No, he had to be at the hearing tomorrow.

On legs as flimsy as sticks, she went to the front door. She rang the bell and waited. In a few seconds Mrs. Groves answered.

Her blue eyes opened wide in delight. Then she laid a finger across her lips for silence. She spoke in a low voice. "You're just what the doctor ordered. Adam is in the library." She stepped back and pointed Cara down the hall.

Cara stepped inside. "Is he ill?"

The housekeeper shook her head and closed the

door. "Go to him." She padded off in her house slippers to her quarters.

In the dark hall Cara stood and listened. Only the sound of the wind moaning in the eaves was audible. She noted the faint glow from the library. Firelight, she thought.

She drew four jerky breaths, then walked along the thick hall runner to the open door of the library.

The fire had burned low, showing only a flicker here and there along a log. Adam sprawled on the long sofa. A brandy snifter and a half-full decanter sat on the coffee table.

She walked into the room, her legs trembling with each step. He swung his head around at her approach. For just a second she glimpsed his soul and saw anguish, then he smiled with a sardonic twist to his lips.

"You got the special delivery," he said.

"Yes."

A taut silence ensued. "Come to gloat?"

She recognized a brave front when she saw one. His jaw was rigid, his face without expression. "No."

He picked up the snifter and took a swallow. "No. You're too decent for that, aren't you?"

"I don't know," she admitted. "We all have our moments of pettiness. We usually take them. Actually I came to thank you."

He gave her a hard glance, then gazed into the fire. "Sure."

"I did. You could have destroyed that letter. I'd never have told anyone."

He surged to his feet, muttering a curse she'd never heard him use before. He drank down the rest of the brandy in the glass. "Do you really think I could have done that?" he snarled.

"Not and live with yourself." She smiled, putting all the tenderness she felt toward him in it. "My father's name is cleared, my mother's and my faith in him vindicated. Thank you for that, Adam."

He stared at her. "You really mean that, don't you? After what my family did to yours, you're thanking me." He shook his head as if past understanding her.

"Adam—"

"When your father was arrested, I was so damned magnanimous." He paced in front of the hearth. "His crime made no difference to *me*. *You* were the one who let it keep us apart. God, what a sanctimonious prig. No wonder you were furious."

"I was confused. I thought if I continued seeing you, I would be disloyal to my family. I—" She stopped, unaware of the words to reach him, to make him forgive himself. "Adam, it wasn't your fault. What happened between our fathers wasn't *our* fault. What happened between us…that was my pride. I was torn by my love for you and my duty to my family."

In the silence she could hear the clock ticking, each second dooming any hope remaining in her heart. Her pride had kept them apart before. Adam's pride would keep them apart now. She'd been a fool to think they could erase past hurts so easily.

"You must hate the very sound of the Clairmont name," he said at last, confirming her doubts.

"No." She sank down on the sofa and clasped her

hands in her lap. "I hated the person who framed my father—"

"Clayton Clairmont," Adam broke in. "*My* father."

"I don't hate him now. I understand. Adam, I do," she insisted when he gave her a disbelieving stare. "He didn't do it for himself, but for the town. He felt an obligation—"

Adam gave a snort of derision. "Pride."

"No...well, maybe that was part of it, but mostly it was a sense of duty to the people who depended on the mill. Adam," she pleaded, "don't you think I understand that?"

"I don't know." He pushed the errant lock of hair that she loved off his forehead with a gesture of weariness. "I don't know what to think anymore. Maybe you'd better tell me exactly why you're here. You could have sent your thanks in a telegram."

Her heart ached for him. She knew what he was going through. "I think Clayton meant for my father or Mr. Wagner to take the blame, but in the end, he couldn't. He altered the books in such a clumsy way no one would believe an accountant had done it. It was a brilliant move on his part."

"So why wasn't he suspected and arrested? Who else had access to the books?"

"I don't know, but I do know this. I forgive him—" She stopped when Adam gave a skeptical snort.

"Do you?" he questioned. "Your life was ruined—"

"It was changed, Adam. Who's to say it was ruined? If I'd stayed here, who can say I would have been happy? I was unsure of your love. I feared you'd come to your senses and dump me."

"I didn't realize you had so little faith in me."

She spread her hands helplessly. "I was young. You were the idol of every girl in town. A summer romance..."

"You didn't think my love would last."

She couldn't refute his statement. Anyway, the past wasn't important. Now she had to help him with the future.

"Adam, I found that letter. Because of me, your life is going to be irrevocably changed."

His brief laughter stopped her. "Not so much. The fifty thousand dollars will have to be repaid to the bonding company. The rest of the money from the furniture will go into modernizing the mill. My personal cash flow will be a bit short for the foreseeable future, but that will change, thanks to your help."

"I'm sorry."

"For what?" he snapped. "For having faith in your father? For being persistent when everyone else had given up? You should get some kind of medal."

"I never wanted to hurt you."

"That doesn't matter."

"It does to me," she said softly, lovingly.

He frowned as he studied her. She saw the hunger leap into his eyes when he lingered at her throat where a pulse hammered in increasing excitement. He still wanted her.

"I'm too tired to argue." He gestured toward the door. "You'd better leave."

He wasn't going to listen to her tonight. Perhaps she should let him get used to the idea of her being there. "Good night," she murmured, putting her heart into the simple utterance. She went to find Mrs. Groves and arrange to use a room for the night.

The housekeeper was delighted. "Don't give up on him," she advised after showing Cara to her old room, which was ready for her. "I expected you," Mrs. Groves explained before Cara could ask. She gave Cara a secretive smile and closed the door.

Cara walked out of the house right behind Adam. She'd eaten breakfast in the kitchen and chatted nervously with Mrs. Groves. He'd gotten himself a cup of coffee, given the two women a harsh glance, then retired to the library until time for the hearing.

Adam gave her an unreadable glance when she unlocked the van and climbed in. She gave him her tenderest smile, loving him with everything in her.

"Look, the hawks," she pointed out, seeing them float over the ridge and into view. Her lucky omen.

Adam watched them, then shrugged and got into the Porsche. She followed him down the mountain. At the courthouse, she walked beside him and sat next to him while the presiding judge and the district attorney reviewed the case. Adam presented the letter.

It was soon over. Adam agreed to refund all monies owed to the insurance company from his father's estate. Taking into account the reasons behind the theft and the fact that all the money had been invested in the mill, there were no further penalties. The case was dismissed.

Cara experienced a vast sense of relief. She schooled herself to patience while they spoke to the judge, the district attorney, the lawyers and finally the reporters, then she walked out the door with him.

On the courthouse steps, she breathed in the pure spring air. "It's over," she murmured. "At last."

Adam stopped and looked at her. "You can leave with a clear conscience. You did what you came here to do."

She clenched her hands together to stop their trembling. He hated her. She'd expected it, but that didn't make it any easier.

"Yes." The word was a mere whisper of sound. She knew the longing was in her eyes as she looked at him.

He'd shut himself away, she realized, past all emotion and all hurt. So had she all those years ago. How could she reach him?

"Adam—"

With a curse, he stepped away from her. Then he abruptly left. He drove off in the flashy red sports car, looking as if he were driving straight into hell.

She stood there on the courthouse steps—where they'd parted so long ago—and relived each of the eight lonely years she'd lived without him. Scanning the sky, she saw two specks far above the valley. She remembered Adam's voice and the way it had sounded years ago when he'd told her he loved her.

She rushed to her van. Adam would never leave Paradise Falls. He was needed too much. He'd never desert the town to follow his own inclinations. He would need someone with him, to comfort him, to give his heart and his body ease. She wanted to be that person.

Was it too late for them? Pain racked her. He was her mate, her one true love. She realized she needed to tell him that. If he rejected her... She couldn't bear the thought.

She raced along the winding road to the mansion. The Porsche was in the drive. She parked and went in.

He was in the library, standing at the window, staring out at the sky. His den, she thought, the place where he went to lick his wounds and rebuild his defenses. When she walked in, he whirled, his manner cold and unwelcoming.

"What are you doing here?" he demanded.

Adam cursed his reaction as his blood clamored at the sight of her. He couldn't stop it. The feeling was raw and wild. It was primitive and instinctive. He needed her, he needed her for days, months, years...and his control was slipping badly. The past few years had been hard; the past few weeks had been impossible.

"I wanted to talk to you," she said.

It was long past the time for words. What had once been, could never be again. He hadn't understood when she'd tried to explain the facts to him. He'd thought only of his need for her. What a sanctimonious fool he'd been, blaming her, thinking her love hadn't been strong enough.

"I wanted to tell you..."

Her lips trembled, and she hesitated, visibly fighting for control. He remembered how her mouth felt under his, giving him all her sweet passion. He stopped himself from reaching for her.

"Say what you have to say, Cara," he advised and heard the harshness in his voice. He'd never managed an even keel when it came to her. She'd been too important in his life. "Then...then you'd better leave."

He should let her know she was on the line where honor fought with need. And his need of her was fast overcoming all else. He glanced toward the sofa. A groan rose to his throat.

A faint blush colored her cheeks. "I don't want to leave. I want to stay. Forever."

At the doubt on Adam's face, Cara's own fled. This was right. She went to him and laid one hand on his chest. He was so warm and alive. Yes, this was right.

He stepped back. "Why?"

She smiled at him. "I think you know."

"Are you feeling sorry for me?" he demanded, then answered the question without waiting for her reply. "Of course you are. You've been through all this—the stares, the way people look away when your eyes meet theirs. That's why you came back. That's why you went to court with me, isn't it?"

"Yes."

His face hardened. "Are you here to comfort me?"

"If you'll let me."

His gaze became ice crystals. "No, thanks."

"I love you."

He gave her a stony glare.

"I was afraid to confess it. When I found the letter

I was afraid if I destroyed it and we married that I might come to hate you later."

"You were about to burn it when I stopped you," he reminded her harshly.

"I know. The past was over. What was the use in bringing it back up? It would only hurt you. And I knew you would hate me for exposing it."

"Your faith in my integrity is overwhelming."

She went on. "I couldn't stand the thought of hurting you or you hating me. I thought it would be better to forget the whole thing, to leave and—" the rest was harder to say "—and get on with my life... without you."

"And what about me?" he demanded with unrelenting hardness.

"I thought you'd go on with your life, too."

He folded his arms across his chest and contemplated her for a long minute. "Just like that?"

"Yes." She couldn't tell him how much the idea hurt.

"I loved you once."

"I know." She closed her eyes in misery, then looked at him resolutely. She'd learned to live without his love. She would have to again. It was clear he hated her.

Cara watched as he pushed a hand through his hair wearily. "Nothing has changed that," he said as if defeated.

She gaped at him.

He smiled without mirth. "Nothing," he repeated. "I thought I was over you. I was curious about your life, sure, but there was nothing left of my feelings.

And then you arrived on a cold Saturday in April and I found nothing had changed.''

''Nothing?'' she questioned, not sure she was hearing right.

''I wanted you the moment you stepped out of that van and walked toward the door.''

''I thought you hated me—''

''No.''

She wasn't sure what to do. He didn't reach for her. Nothing about him invited her touch. She decided to be bold. ''Then why should I leave when I want to stay with all my heart?''

A light blazed in his eyes. ''Be sure,'' he said. ''I don't think I can let you go a second time.''

''I am.'' She smiled as bravely as she could and waited.

Adam drew a deep breath. ''We've had some hard knocks, but if you'll take a chance…I'll love you for as long as I live.'' His gaze grew tender. ''My father taught me. He loved my mother and he made sure she never doubted it. I'd love you like that. If you have faith in my love, we can make it.''

She had one more question. ''Adam, if life becomes too hard, mightn't you hate me for exposing your father?''

''No.'' There was no uncertainty in him.

With that one word, Cara knew that Adam had made his peace with his father in his own heart. He'd forgiven him. As with her, there'd be no rancor left to build into bitterness.

''If you love me enough to spare my feelings, why

do you find it so hard to believe in my love?'' he continued.

The words were there, but so were the tears. They filled her throat. She closed her eyes, opened them and found him still watching her, waiting for her. There was no mistaking the need nor the hunger. They burned there in the depths of his stormy gray eyes—strong, urgent, steady. Along with his love. She reached for him.

"I do believe," she said. "Adam, I do."

Adam took her into his arms and held her. He felt a tremor course through her and held her tighter.

"I thought we'd never reach this moment," he murmured, relief sweeping through him, clear to his soul.

"It's taken a long time for me to trust your love," she whispered. "I'm sorry for that."

"It's finally over," he said, taking her face between his hands and gazing into her eyes. "We still have some legal and financial tangles to unravel, but for us, the doubts are gone...finally."

"Yes." Cara smiled, tremulous but confident of their future. It would all work now. They were truly free of the past.

"Welcome to Paradise Falls," he murmured. "You've come home at last."

She sighed and raised her mouth to his. The winter of their separation had been long and lonely for both of them. But now it was over. And it was spring—a time of renewal, a time for mating and other important rituals.

Adam gathered her close, his kiss deep and welcoming.

Her heart soared.

* * * * *

American HEROES
AGAINST ALL ODDS

Please address questions and book requests to: Harlequin Reader Service U.S.: 3010 Walden Ave.,
P.O. Box 1325, Buffalo, NY 14269 CAN.: P.O. Box 609, Fort Erie, Ont. L2A 5X3   PAHGEN

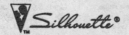

FOUR UNIQUE SERIES
FOR EVERY WOMAN YOU ARE...

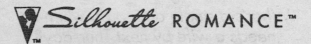

These entertaining, tender and involving love stories
celebrate the spirit of pure romance.

Desire features strong heroes and spirited heroines
who come together in a highly passionate,
emotionally powerful and always provocative read.

Silhouette SPECIAL EDITION

For every woman who dreams of life, love and family,
these are the romances in which she makes
her dreams come true.

Dive into the pages of Intimate Moments and experience
adventure and excitement in these complex
and dramatic romances.

Silhouette ROMANCE™

What's a single dad to do when he needs a wife by next Thursday?

Who's a confirmed bachelor to call when he finds a baby on his doorstep?

How does a plain Jane in love with her gorgeous boss get him to notice her?

From classic love stories to romantic comedies to emotional heart tuggers, **Silhouette Romance** offers six irresistible novels every month by some of your favorite authors!

Come experience compelling stories by beloved bestsellers **Diana Palmer, Stella Bagwell, Sandra Steffen, Susan Meier** and **Marie Ferrarella,** to name just a few—and more authors sure to become favorites as well!!

Silhouette Romance—always emotional, always enjoyable, always about love!

Attention Silhouette Readers:

Romance is just one click away!

online book serials

- *Exclusive* to our web site, get caught up in both the daily and weekly online installments of new romance stories.

- Try the Writing Round Robin. Contribute a chapter to a story created by our members. Plus, winners will get prizes.

romantic travel

- Want to know where the best place to kiss in New York City is, or which restaurant in Los Angeles is the most romantic? Check out our Romantic Hot Spots for the scoop.

- Share your travel tips and stories with us on the romantic travel message boards.

romantic reading library

- Relax as you read our collection of Romantic Poetry.

- Take a peek at the Top 10 Most Romantic Lines!

Visit us online at

www.eHarlequin.com

on Women.com Networks

"No," said Jane, "they are family. They have a right to know. And then if they still think it would be better for me to go to them why—it will be all right! They are *my* family now, you know!"

"You dear!" breathed Kent softly. "Well, all right. Suppose we make it tomorrow after closing?"

"Lovely!" said Jane, her eyes sparkling. "I told the gardener's wife to wash the windows, and dust and take off the chair covers. Maybe Audrey would like to help us put up the curtains. Then it will look really livable."

"Of course she will, dear little housewife! I didn't know you were wise to those things."

But Jane only laughed.

"Perhaps you'd better get wise too," she said. "You might do something about getting the gas and electricity turned on."

"I'll attend to that, lady, right away today," he said humbly.

So the Havenner family, including the father, because he utterly refused to be left out of such an important occasion, arrived at the old Scarlett home in state, a few minutes after Jane and Kent got there, on Saturday afternoon.

They stared in wide-eyed amazement at the beautiful old house and grounds, and there was utmost approval and wonder in their eyes as they came up the brick walk to the porch.

"Why, Jane, dear!" said mother Havenner. "Such a wonderful old place! Of course you would want to be married here! How marvelous that you have it!"

Then they went inside.

Jane had had time to put flowers from the garden in most of the rooms, and it looked so homey they all exclaimed.

It was almost like a gathering of the two families, as they sat down in the big living room and looked up at the great oil-paintings while Jane explained who they all were, and then got out the old album which included her mother's wedding pictures.

And while they put up the living room curtains of delicate old yellowed lace, and admired everything, they settled all the plans for the wedding.

It was agreed that it should be a quiet wedding, no fuss and show. Just the dearest, most intimate friends, invited by note or called up on the telephone, and then the Havenners would give a small reception in their city house afterward to introduce their new daughter a trifle more formally to their acquaintances.

"Oh, it's lovely, *lovely,* Jane!" said Audrey, patting the filmy folds of the last curtain. "And how I do *love* my new sister!" and she caught Jane in a warm embrace and whirled her around the room gaily. "What a grand time you and I are going to have! I never supposed my brother would have the sense to pick out such a wonderful girl as you are!"

They would all have spoiled her if Jane hadn't been through so many hard things that she was impervious to spoiling.

And just before they turned out the lights and left for the night Audrey looked around the lovely room and said:

"Say, Jane, this would be a grand place to have a Bible class sometime! I just know Pat would enjoy teaching in a place like this!"

"Wouldn't it?" said Jane with a sparkle in her eyes. Audrey had been to the Thursday night Bible class with them this week and Jane had been longing to know how she liked it. "I have been thinking about that. When we get acquainted with the people around here perhaps we can get a group together. Wouldn't that be wonderful?"

"It certainly would," said Audrey.

As the days went by Jane flitted here and there in the store, picking out a few pretty clothes. The green coat she had wanted so long she could now buy outright, and not have to arrange for it by installments. She made it the basis of her fall outfit. A lovely green wool dress, and another of crepe. A brown wool, a lighter brown silk, some bright blouses, and then a couple of gay prints for morning around the house. How she enjoyed getting them together, and all the little accessories of her modest trousseau, and realizing that she could pay for them and not need to worry lest there wouldn't be enough over to pay her board for another week. Her heart was continually singing at the great things the Lord had done for her.

It was a pretty wedding, no ostentation, no fuss.

There were about fifty guests present, most of them relatives and intimate friends of the Havenner family. A few from the store, Miss Leech, Mr. Windle, Mr. Clark and his little girl, Hilda and the two other girls from the button counter.

Pat Whitney married them, and Audrey was the maid of honor. The rest of the wedding procession they skipped.

Jane wore her mother's wedding dress and veil and looked very sweet and quaint in the rich satin and real lace, a trifle yellowed from the years.

As the bride stood beneath her grandmother's portrait, some people thought they saw a resemblance between the two.

Mr. Havenner went about beaming, almost as if he were getting married himself. Hilda and the two girls from the button counter sat around adoringly and watched th erstwhile co-laborer going about these sweet old rooms, mistress of it all, wife of that "perfectly swell" looking young lawyer. They thought of Jane going untiringly about her work behind the counter, and wondered wistfully if a like change could ever come to them.

And when it was all over, and the wedding supper eaten, the bridal cake cut and distributed, Jane went upstairs throwing down her bouquet straight into the arms of her new sister-in-law, who stood at the foot of the stairs with Pat looking up.

Jane went into the room where she had stayed when she was a little girl visiting in that house so long ago, and changed to her new lovely green suit. Then she and Kent slipped down the back stairs and out through a basement door to Kent's car, which was hidden in a back street. The wedding guests, waiting to see them off with old shoes and rice in the decked-up car that stood before the door, were unaware that they were gone.

As they rounded the corner and caught another glimpse of the lighted windows Jane turned to look.

"It's a dear house," she breathed.

"Yes!" said Kent. "I love it too, you know."

She nestled toward him and slipped her arm inside his.

"I'm glad!" she said softly. And then after a minute

added: "It will always make me think of my Heavenly mansion. It seems just as if it was sent me at a time when I had nothing, as a sort of picture-promise of our home in Heaven. It's just a place where God wants us to be happy and work for Him while we are waiting for the Heavenly home."

Then softly she began to sing, and Kent chanted with her, as they drove out into their new life:

> "Oh Lord, you know,
> We have no friend like you,
> If Heaven is not our Home,
> Oh Lord, what shall we do?
> The angels beckon us
> To Heaven's open door,
> We can't feel at home
> In this world any more."